Jesse Tree Ornaments

Advent Coloring Activities and Craft Projects for Kids with Bible Stories for the Jesse Tree Symbols

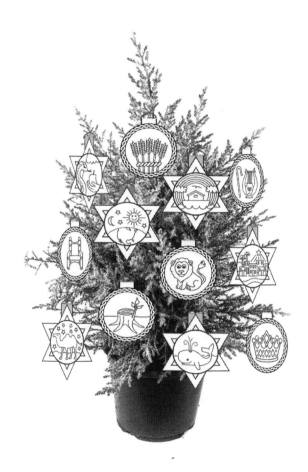

Kathryn Marcellino

Abundant Life Publishing

ISBN 978-1-944158-00-2 (Paperback)

Abundant Life Publishing
PO Box 3753
Modesto, CA 95352
email: km@AbundantLifePublishing.com
www.AbundantLifePublishing.com

Printed in the USA

Table of Contents

History of the Jesse Tree 1

The Jesse Tree Symbols 1

Ideas for Making and Using the Ornaments 1

Making the Jesse Tree Ornaments 2

Options for Displaying the Ornaments 2

Jesse Tree Symbols and Ornaments to Color 4

Instructions for Paper Jesse Tree 53

Pattern for Paper Jesse Tree 55

Optional Star for the Top of the Tree 63

Bible Stories and Scripture Passages for each Jesse Tree Ornament 65

    December 1: The Story of Creation 66

    December 2: The Fall of Adam and Eve 68

    December 3: Noah and the Ark 69

    December 4: Abraham the Patriarch and Sarah his Wife 70

    December 5: Isaac, son of Abraham 71

    December 6: Jacob, son of Isaac 72

    December 7: Joseph, son of Jacob 73

    December 8: Moses and the Passover 74

    December 9: Moses and the Ten Commandments 75

    December 10: Ruth and Boaz 76

    December 11: Samuel the Prophet 77

    December 12: Branch of Jesse 78

    December 13: King David 79

    December 14: King Solomon 80

    December 15: Elijah the Prophet 81

    December 16: Jonah and the Whale 83

    December 17: Isaiah the Prophet 84

    December 18: Daniel and the Lion 85

    December 19: Mary, Mother of Jesus 86

    December 20: Joseph, Stepfather of Jesus 88

    December 21: John the Baptist 89

    December 22: Bethlehem, the birthplace of Jesus 90

    December 23: Angels Proclaim the Birth of Jesus 91

    December 24: The Birth of Christ on Christmas Day 92

Blank Ornaments: 93

All Ornaments on Two Pages 101

History of the Jesse Tree

Historically the Tree of Jesse showed the genealogy of Jesus Christ using art and/or symbols representing the ancestors of Christ. There have been various numbers of symbols and types of art used over the centuries.

The name Jesse Tree comes from a Bible passage describing the descent of the Messiah from Jesse in Isaiah 11:1: "A shoot will come out of the stock of Jesse, and a branch out of his roots will bear fruit." The Gospels in Luke 3:23-38 and in Matthew 1:1-17 have genealogies of Jesus Christ.

The Jesse Tree Symbols

The Jesse Tree symbols chosen from many possibilities for this book are original illustrations showing some important figures and events from Creation to the birth of Jesus Christ. Blank ornament templates or patterns can also be found at the back of this book if you want to draw some of your own favorites, especially if you want additional ornaments for all the days of Advent.

Ideas for Making and Using the Ornaments

This book has 24 ornaments to be used from December 1st through December 24th. Each ornament in this book has three optional designs to make and color. The cover of this book also has 24 ornaments that also can be cut out and used for making a Jesse Tree if desired. After coloring, the ornaments can be displayed in various ways.

Suggested use: After making the ornaments you can read the Scriptural passage on the back of the two-sided ornaments for each day beginning December 1st and ending with Christmas Eve. Then hang the ornament on a tree for display. Longer Bible stories and Scriptural passages for each ornament start on page 66 to learn more about some of the important people and events leading up to the birth of Jesus Christ.

Making the Jesse Tree Ornaments

The following pages have three ornament styles for each of the 24 days of December before Christmas. Each ornament may be cut out and colored with crayons, pencils, or felt tip markers. Ideas for colors can be seen on the cover of the book. For two sided ornaments, fold the ornaments on the dashed lines so the colored side is facing out.

For the two-sided ornaments, there are various options for hanging them on the tree. A ribbon, piece of yarn, or string could be put through the loop created at the top, or a hole can also be punched about $\frac{1}{4}$ inch from the top of the ornament and a Christmas tree hook, ribbon, string, or piece of yarn can be inserted through the punched hole. The two-sided ornaments can be glued, stapled, or taped together using double-sided tape.

The single-sided ornament could also have a single hole punched near the top. These could be signed and dated on the back by the coloring artist. These ornaments can also be used on your Christmas tree.

The ornaments can also be laminated if desired before punching the hole in the top for hanging. First color each ornament and cut them out leaving the black line around the edges. Laminate them and then cut them out again leaving at about $\frac{1}{4}$ inch of lamination around the edges.

Options for Displaying the Ornaments

Idea #1: Make a 3-dimensional paper tree from construction paper or poster board. Instructions and a pattern are on page 57 of this book.

Idea #2: Use a small 2-3 feet artificial or live Christmas tree.

Idea #3: A tree can also be made from a tree branch, Manzanita, or other bush about 2-3 feet high, preferably one with a strong center trunk with side branches. The branch can be placed in a small bucket or container filled with rocks or dirt and covered with cloth or paper to decorate it.

Options continued:

Idea #4: A tree can also be cut out from paper or felt, fastened to cardboard or a bulletin board, and then the ornaments can be tacked to it.

Idea #5: The ornaments could also be displayed without a tree by simply tacking them to a bulletin board or hanging them on a long string like a clothes line.

Tree made out of bare branches put in a container filled with sand, rocks, or dirt.

Tree made out of colored construction paper or poster board using the pattern found in this book.

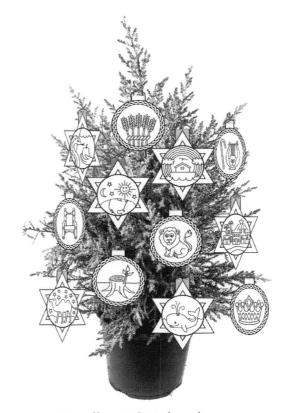

Small artificial or live Christmas tree or similar plant.

Jesse Tree Symbols and Ornaments to Color

The following pages have ornaments to color and cut out.
Each ornament has three formats to choose from or to mix and match.

Ornaments for December 1:
The Story of Creation

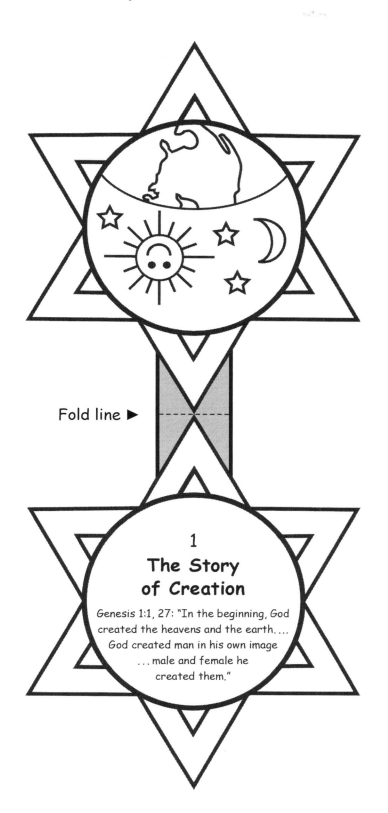

Fold line ▶

1
**The Story
of Creation**

Genesis 1:1, 27: "In the beginning, God
created the heavens and the earth....
God created man in his own image
...male and female he
created them."

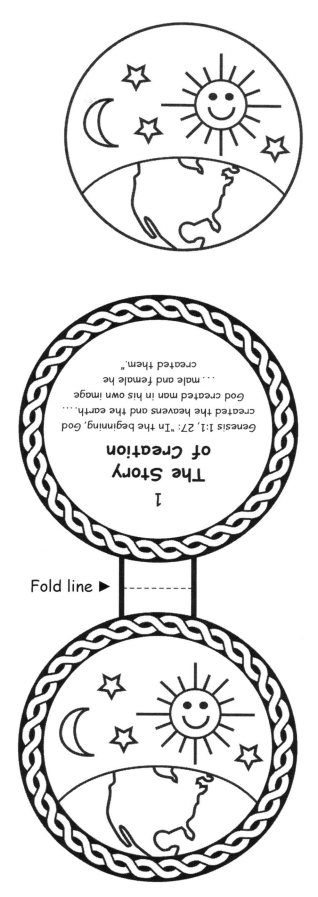

Fold line ▶

1
The Story
of Creation

Genesis 1:1, 27: "In the beginning, God
created the heavens and the earth....
God created man in his own image
...male and female he
created them."

6

Ornaments for December 2:
The Fall of Adam and Eve

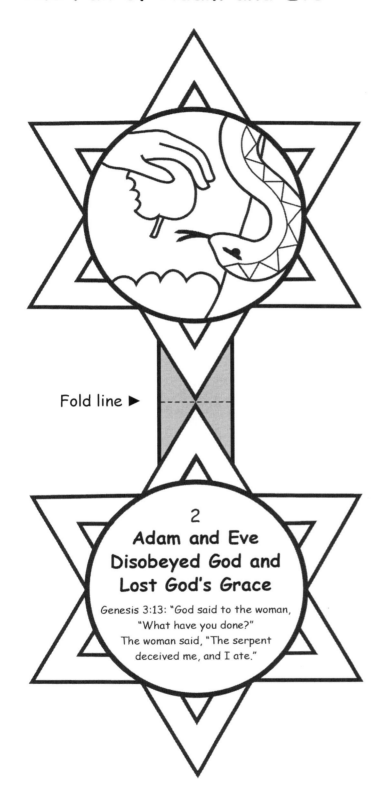

2
Adam and Eve Disobeyed God and Lost God's Grace

Genesis 3:13: "God said to the woman, "What have you done?" The woman said, "The serpent deceived me, and I ate."

Fold line ▶

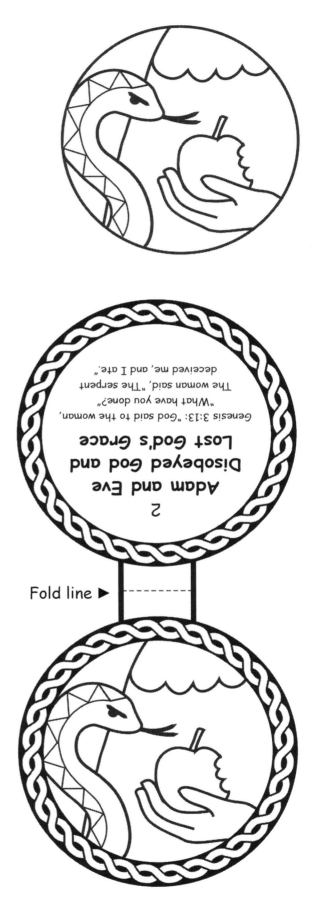

Fold line ▶

Ornaments for December 3:
Noah and the Ark

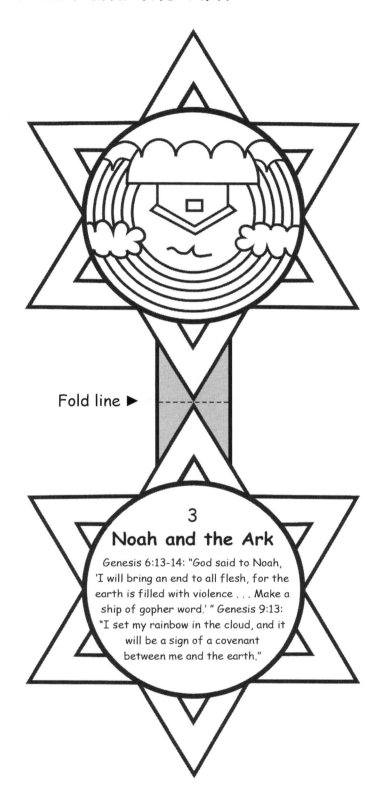

Fold line ▶

3
Noah and the Ark

Genesis 6:13-14: "God said to Noah,
'I will bring an end to all flesh, for the
earth is filled with violence . . . Make a
ship of gopher word.' " Genesis 9:13:
"I set my rainbow in the cloud, and it
will be a sign of a covenant
between me and the earth."

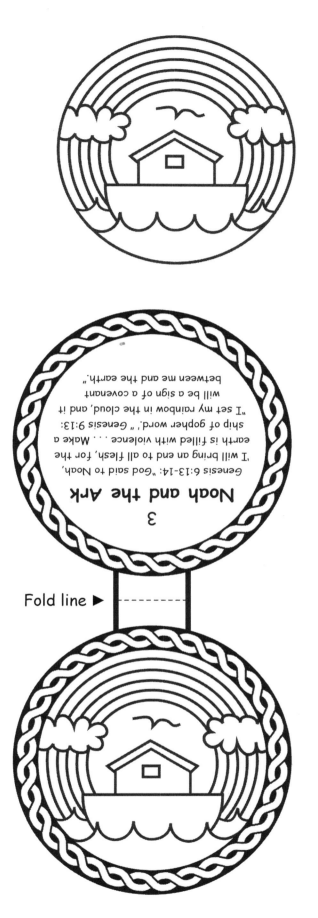

Fold line ▶

9

Ornaments for December 4:
Abraham

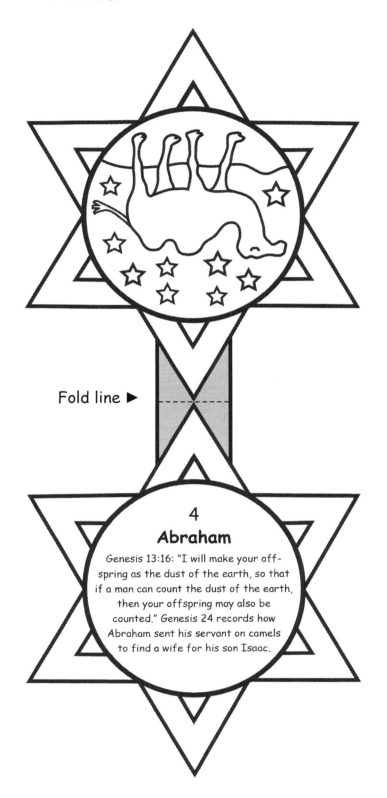

4
Abraham

Genesis 13:16: "I will make your offspring as the dust of the earth, so that
if a man can count the dust of the earth,
then your offspring may also be
counted." Genesis 24 records how
Abraham sent his servant on camels
to find a wife for his son Isaac.

Fold line ▶

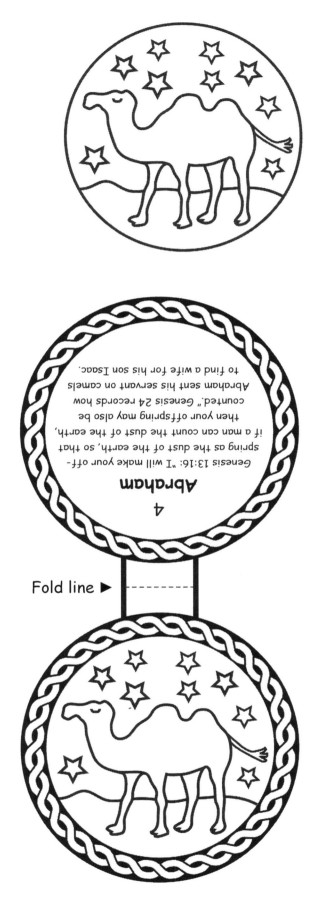

Fold line ▶

Ornaments for December 5:
Isaac, son of Abraham

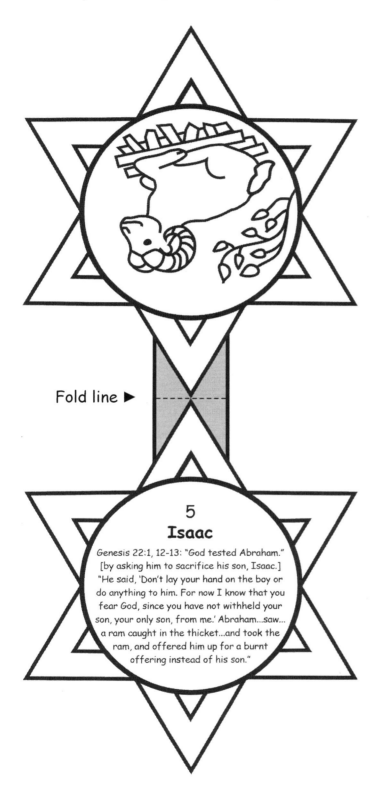

Fold line ▶

5
Isaac

Genesis 22:1, 12-13: "God tested Abraham."
[by asking him to sacrifice his son, Isaac.]
"He said, 'Don't lay your hand on the boy or
do anything to him. For now I know that you
fear God, since you have not withheld your
son, your only son, from me.' Abraham...saw...
a ram caught in the thicket...and took the
ram, and offered him up for a burnt
offering instead of his son."

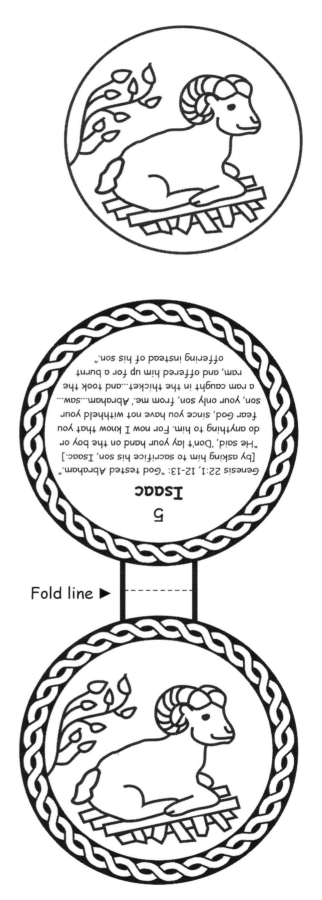

Fold line ▶

Ornaments for December 6:
Jacob, son of Isaac

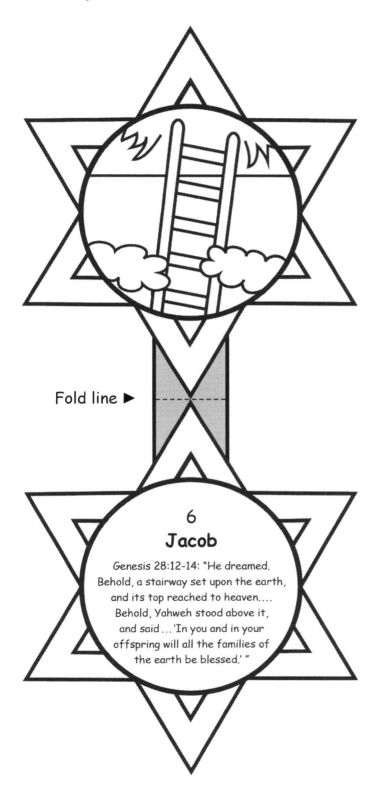

Fold line ▶

6
Jacob

Genesis 28:12-14: "He dreamed.
Behold, a stairway set upon the earth,
and its top reached to heaven....
Behold, Yahweh stood above it,
and said ... 'In you and in your
offspring will all the families of
the earth be blessed.' "

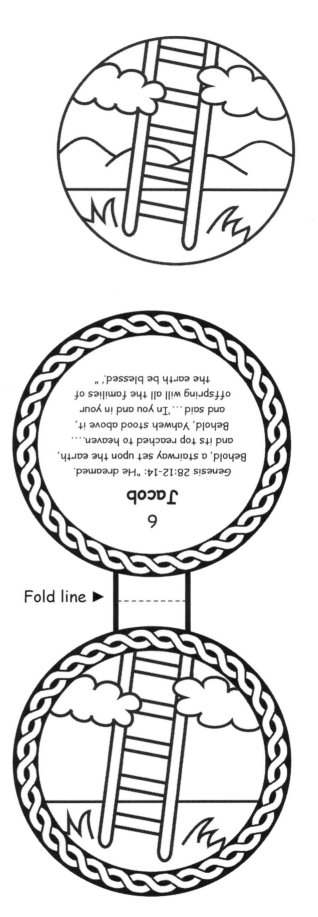

Fold line ▶

Ornaments for December 7:
Joseph, son of Jacob

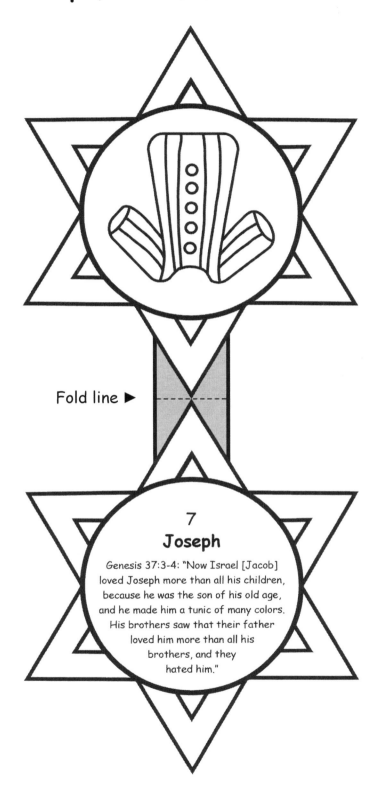

Fold line ▶

7
Joseph

Genesis 37:3-4: "Now Israel [Jacob]
loved Joseph more than all his children,
because he was the son of his old age,
and he made him a tunic of many colors.
His brothers saw that their father
loved him more than all his
brothers, and they
hated him."

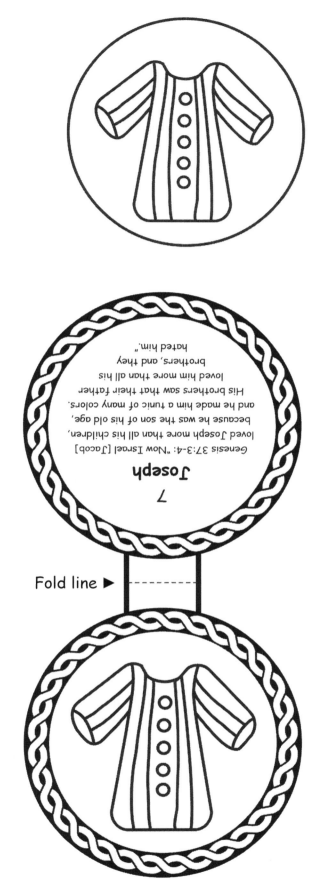

7
Joseph

Genesis 37:3-4: "Now Israel [Jacob]
loved Joseph more than all his children,
because he was the son of his old age,
and he made him a tunic of many colors.
His brothers saw that their father
loved him more than all his
brothers, and they
hated him."

Fold line ▶

Ornaments for December 8:
Moses and the Passover

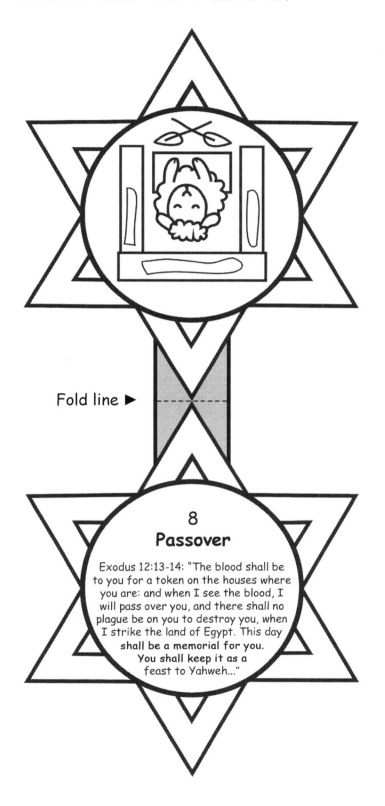

Fold line ▶

8
Passover

Exodus 12:13-14: "The blood shall be to you for a token on the houses where you are: and when I see the blood, I will pass over you, and there shall no plague be on you to destroy you, when I strike the land of Egypt. This day shall be a memorial for you. You shall keep it as a feast to Yahweh..."

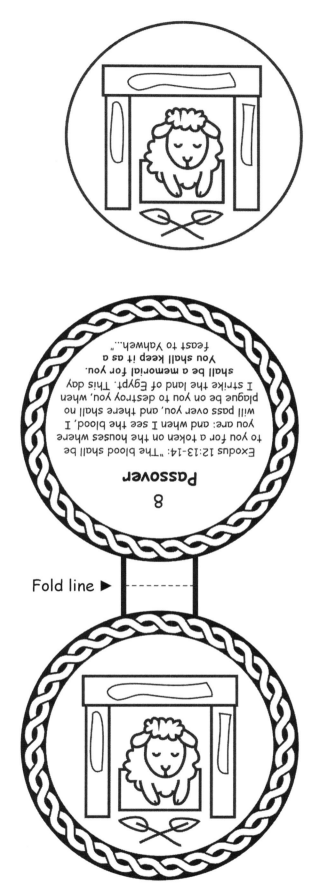

8
Passover

Exodus 12:13-14: "The blood shall be to you for a token on the houses where you are: and when I see the blood, I will pass over you, and there shall no plague be on you to destroy you, when I strike the land of Egypt. This day shall be a memorial for you. You shall keep it as a feast to Yahweh..."

Fold line ▶

Ornaments for December 9:
Moses and the
Ten Commandments

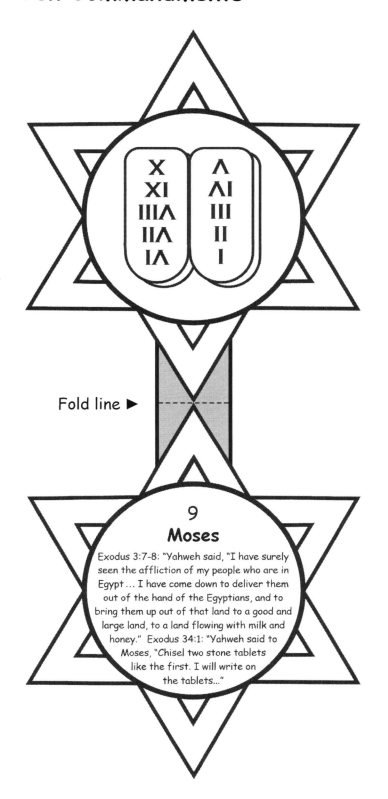

Fold line ▶

9
Moses

Exodus 3:7-8: "Yahweh said, "I have surely seen the affliction of my people who are in Egypt … I have come down to deliver them out of the hand of the Egyptians, and to bring them up out of that land to a good and large land, to a land flowing with milk and honey." Exodus 34:1: "Yahweh said to Moses, "Chisel two stone tablets like the first. I will write on the tablets…"

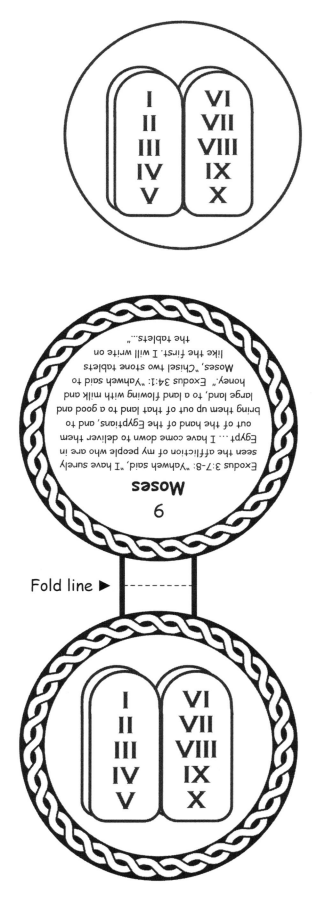

Fold line ▶

Ornaments for December 10: Ruth and Boaz

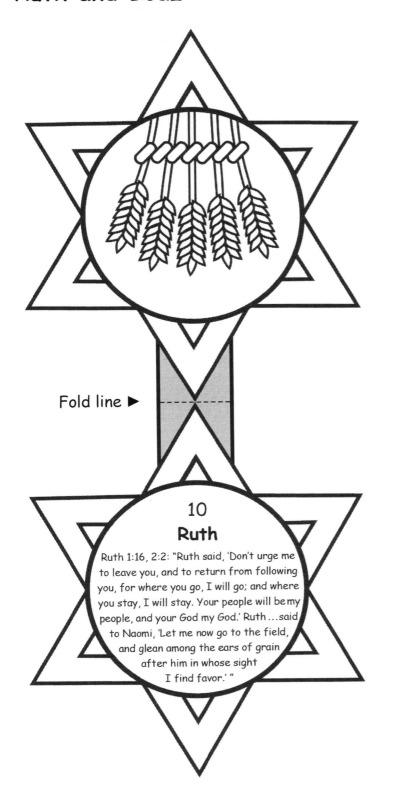

Fold line ▶

10
Ruth

Ruth 1:16, 2:2: "Ruth said, 'Don't urge me to leave you, and to return from following you, for where you go, I will go; and where you stay, I will stay. Your people will be my people, and your God my God.' Ruth ...said to Naomi, 'Let me now go to the field, and glean among the ears of grain after him in whose sight I find favor.' "

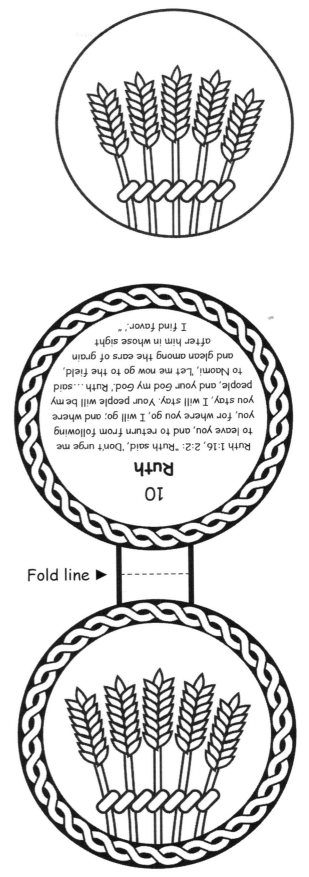

Fold line ▶

Ornaments for December 11: Samuel the Prophet

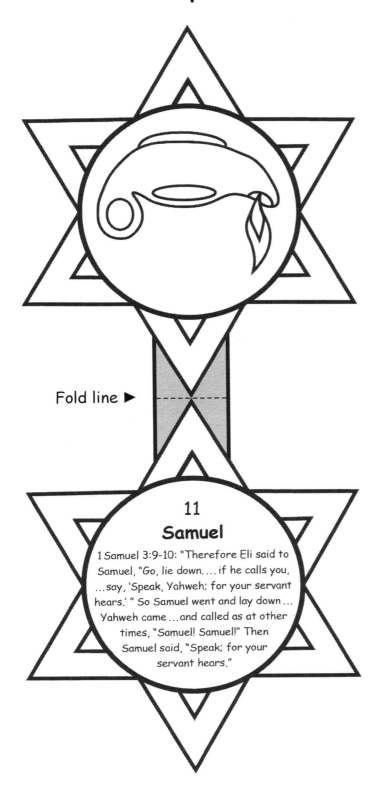

Fold line ▶

11
Samuel

1 Samuel 3:9-10: "Therefore Eli said to Samuel, "Go, lie down. . . . if he calls you, . . . say, 'Speak, Yahweh; for your servant hears.' " So Samuel went and lay down . . . Yahweh came . . . and called as at other times, "Samuel! Samuel!" Then Samuel said, "Speak; for your servant hears."

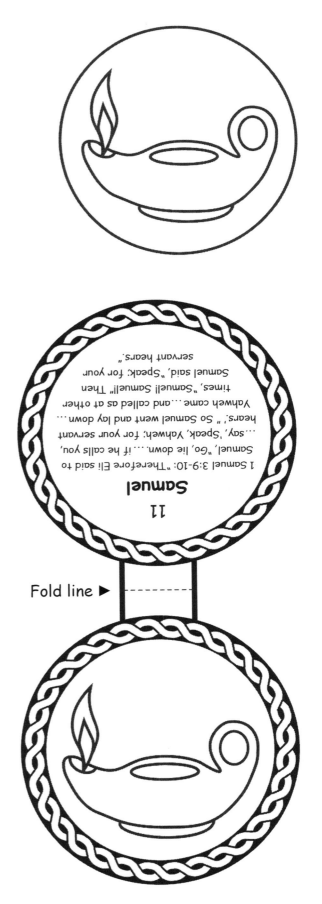

Fold line ▶

Ornaments for December 12: Branch of Jesse

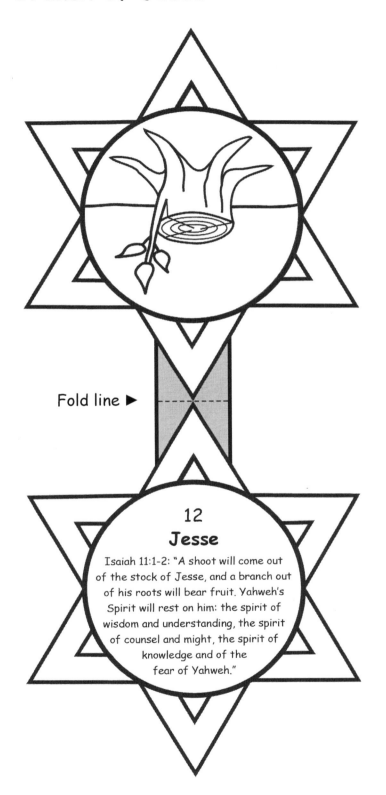

Fold line ▶

12
Jesse

Isaiah 11:1-2: "A shoot will come out
of the stock of Jesse, and a branch out
of his roots will bear fruit. Yahweh's
Spirit will rest on him: the spirit of
wisdom and understanding, the spirit
of counsel and might, the spirit of
knowledge and of the
fear of Yahweh."

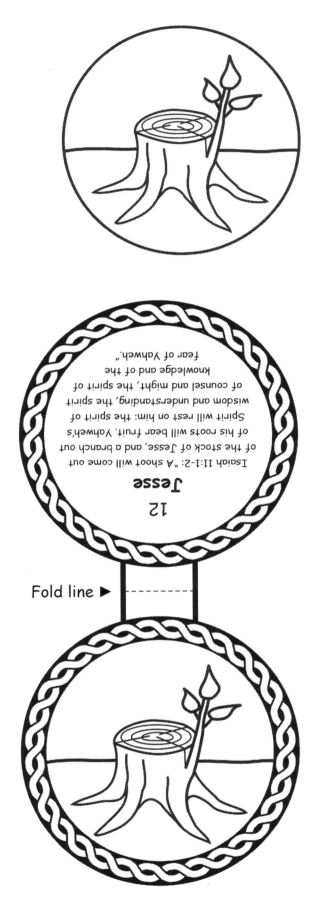

12
Jesse

Isaiah 11:1-2: "A shoot will come out
of the stock of Jesse, and a branch out
of his roots will bear fruit. Yahweh's
Spirit will rest on him: the spirit of
wisdom and understanding, the spirit
of counsel and might, the spirit of
knowledge and of the
fear of Yahweh."

Fold line ▶

27

Ornaments for December 13:
King David

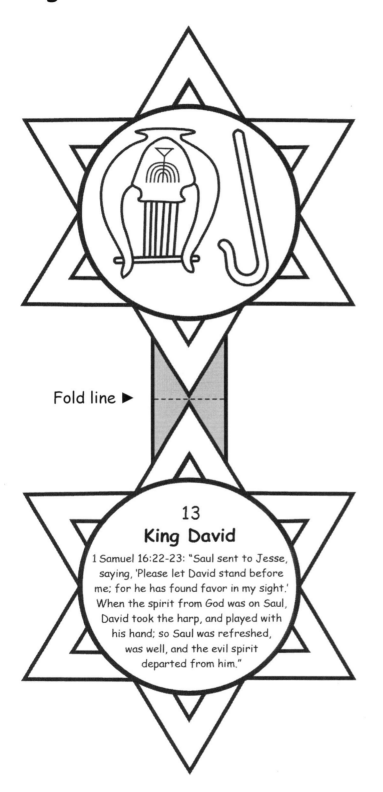

13
King David

1 Samuel 16:22-23: "Saul sent to Jesse, saying, 'Please let David stand before me; for he has found favor in my sight.' When the spirit from God was on Saul, David took the harp, and played with his hand; so Saul was refreshed, was well, and the evil spirit departed from him."

Fold line ▶

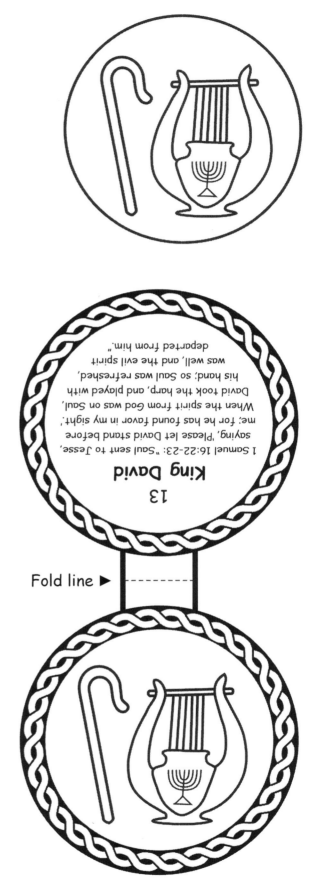

Fold line ▶

Ornaments for December 14:
King Solomon

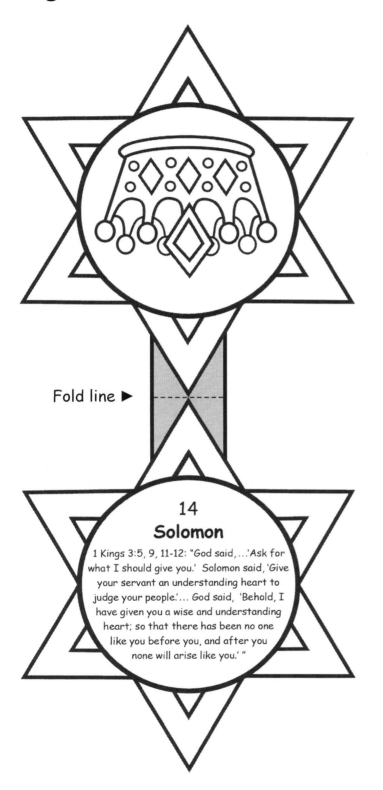

Fold line ▶

14
Solomon

1 Kings 3:5, 9, 11-12: "God said, ...'Ask for what I should give you.' Solomon said, 'Give your servant an understanding heart to judge your people.'... God said, 'Behold, I have given you a wise and understanding heart; so that there has been no one like you before you, and after you none will arise like you.' "

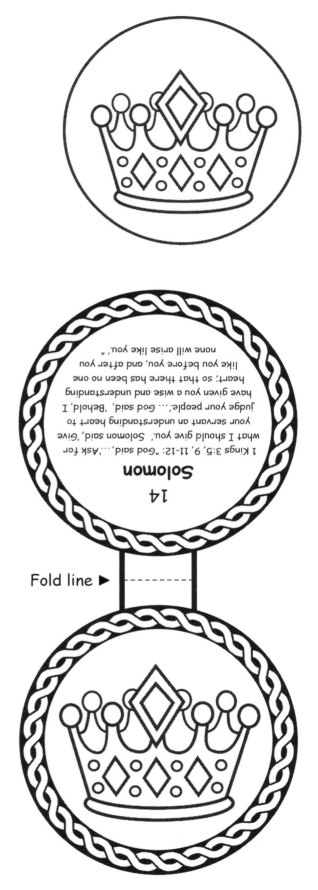

Fold line ▶

31

Ornaments for December 15:
Elijah the Prophet

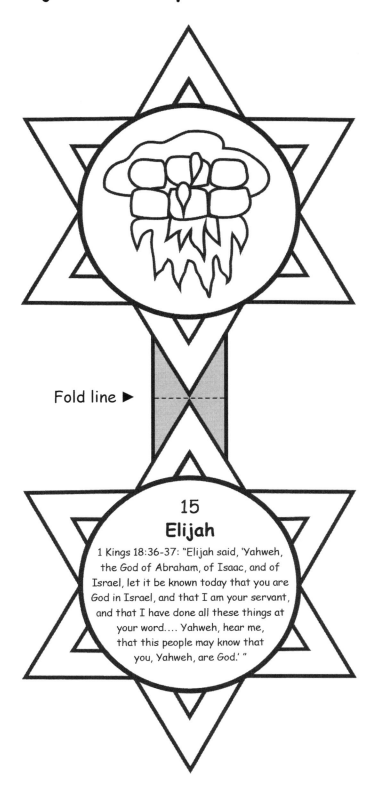

Fold line ▶

15
Elijah

1 Kings 18:36-37: "Elijah said, 'Yahweh, the God of Abraham, of Isaac, and of Israel, let it be known today that you are God in Israel, and that I am your servant, and that I have done all these things at your word.... Yahweh, hear me, that this people may know that you, Yahweh, are God.' "

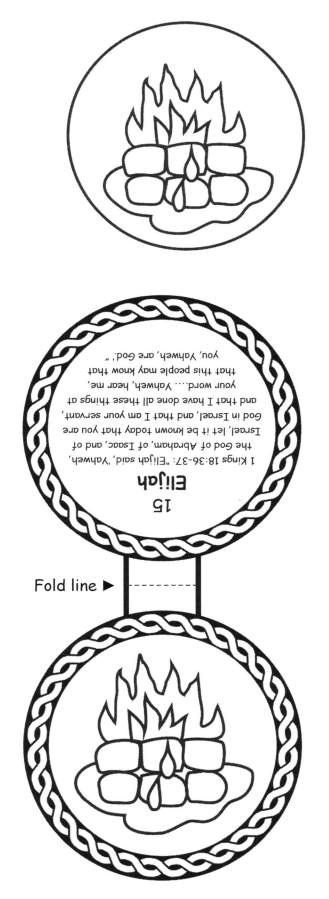

Fold line ▶

Ornaments for December 16: Jonah and the Whale

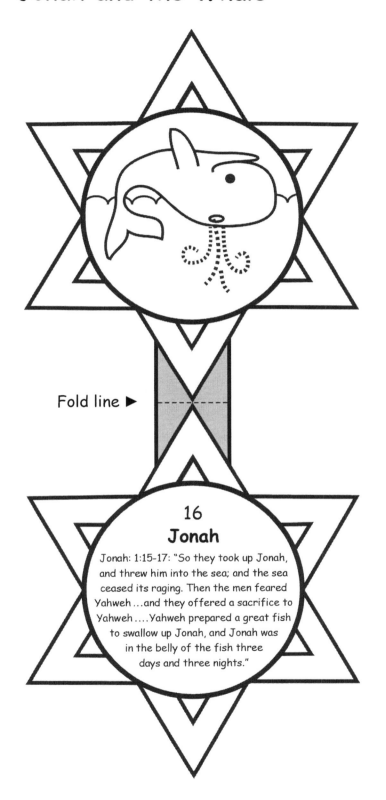

Fold line ▶

16
Jonah

Jonah: 1:15-17: "So they took up Jonah, and threw him into the sea; and the sea ceased its raging. Then the men feared Yahweh…and they offered a sacrifice to Yahweh….Yahweh prepared a great fish to swallow up Jonah, and Jonah was in the belly of the fish three days and three nights."

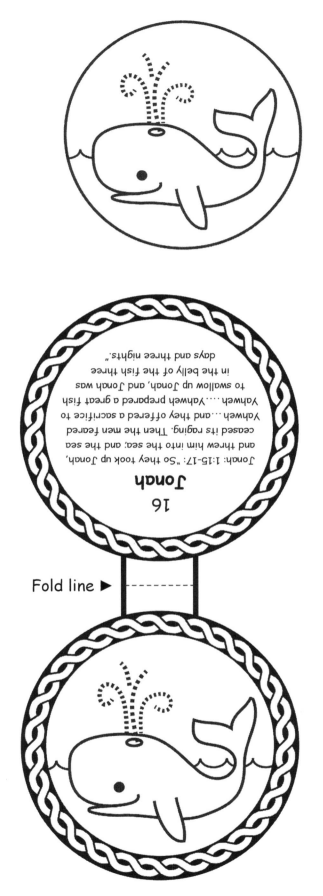

Jonah: 1:15-17: "So they took up Jonah, and threw him into the sea; and the sea ceased its raging. Then the men feared Yahweh…and they offered a sacrifice to Yahweh….Yahweh prepared a great fish to swallow up Jonah, and Jonah was in the belly of the fish three days and three nights."

Jonah
16

Fold line ▶

Ornaments for December 17:
Isaiah the Prophet

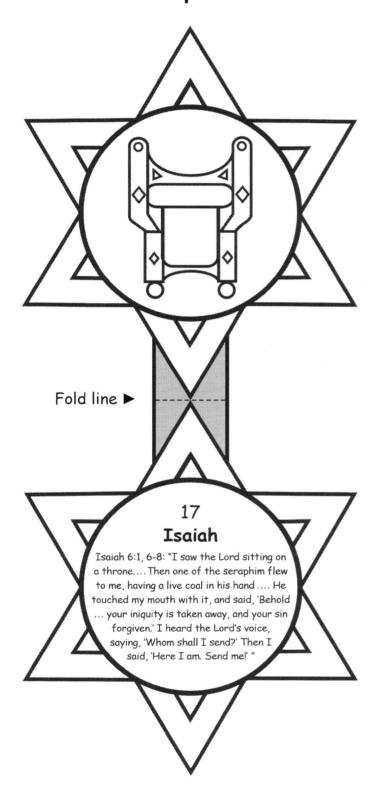

Fold line ▶

17
Isaiah

Isaiah 6:1, 6-8: "I saw the Lord sitting on a throne.... Then one of the seraphim flew to me, having a live coal in his hand.... He touched my mouth with it, and said, 'Behold ... your iniquity is taken away, and your sin forgiven.' I heard the Lord's voice, saying, 'Whom shall I send?' Then I said, 'Here I am. Send me!' "

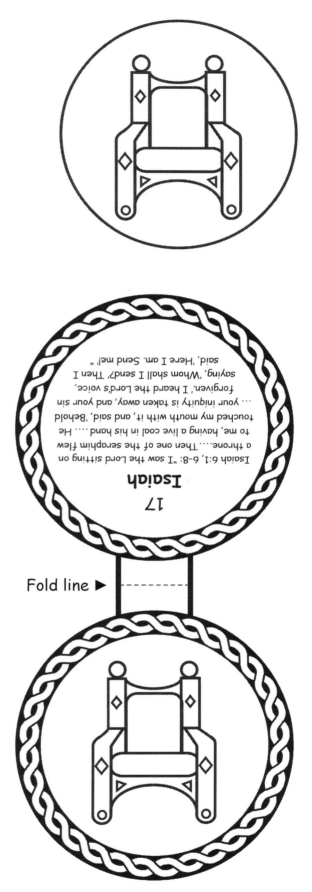

Fold line ▶

Ornaments for December 18:
Daniel and the Lions

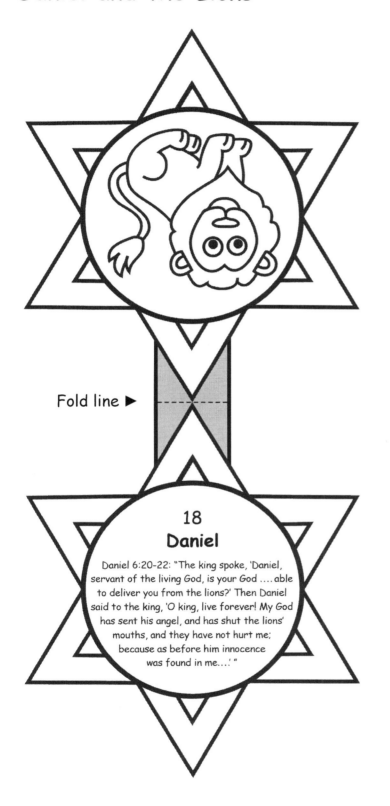

Fold line ▶

18
Daniel

Daniel 6:20-22: "The king spoke, 'Daniel, servant of the living God, is your God ....able to deliver you from the lions?' Then Daniel said to the king, 'O king, live forever! My God has sent his angel, and has shut the lions' mouths, and they have not hurt me; because as before him innocence was found in me....' "

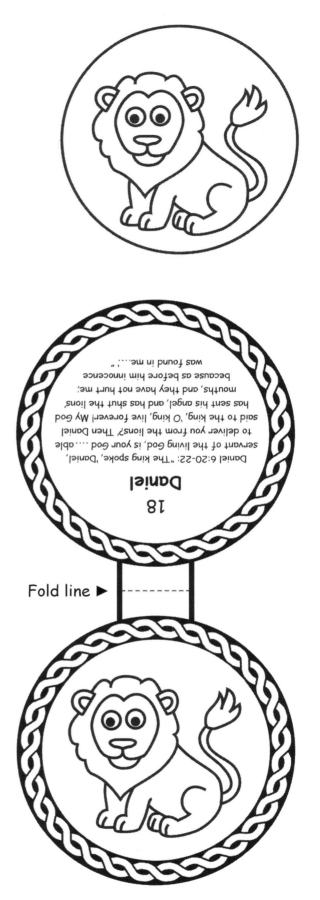

Fold line ▶

39

Ornaments for December 19:
Mary, Mother of Jesus

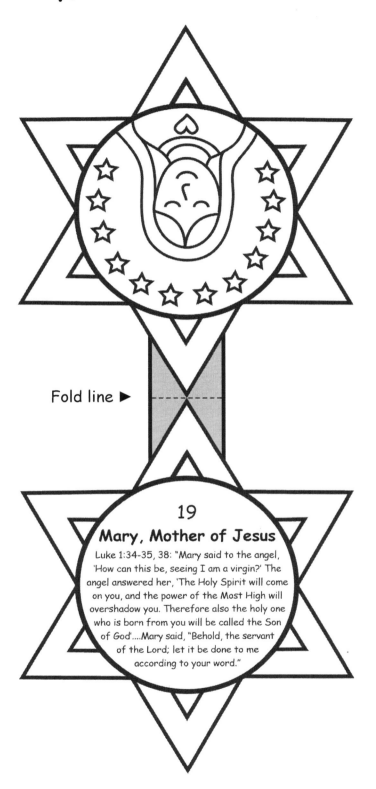

Fold line ▶

19
Mary, Mother of Jesus

Luke 1:34-35, 38: "Mary said to the angel, 'How can this be, seeing I am a virgin?' The angel answered her, 'The Holy Spirit will come on you, and the power of the Most High will overshadow you. Therefore also the holy one who is born from you will be called the Son of God'....Mary said, "Behold, the servant of the Lord; let it be done to me according to your word."

Fold line ▶

Ornaments for December 20:
Joseph, Stepfather of Jesus

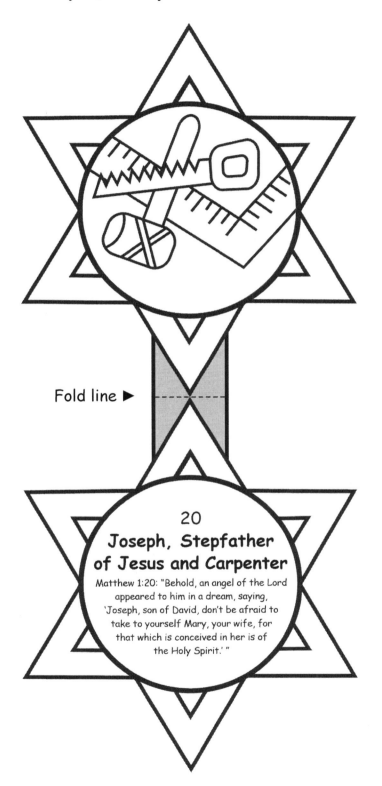

Fold line ▶

20
Joseph, Stepfather of Jesus and Carpenter

Matthew 1:20: "Behold, an angel of the Lord appeared to him in a dream, saying, 'Joseph, son of David, don't be afraid to take to yourself Mary, your wife, for that which is conceived in her is of the Holy Spirit.' "

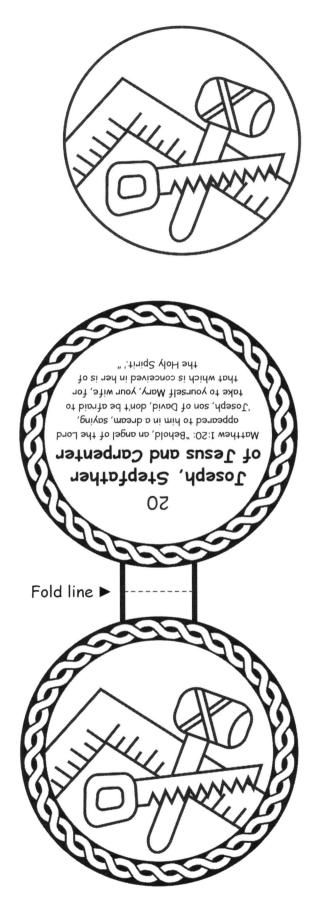

20
Joseph, Stepfather of Jesus and Carpenter

Matthew 1:20: "Behold, an angel of the Lord appeared to him in a dream, saying, 'Joseph, son of David, don't be afraid to take to yourself Mary, your wife, for that which is conceived in her is of the Holy Spirit.' "

Fold line ▶

Ornaments for December 21: John the Baptist

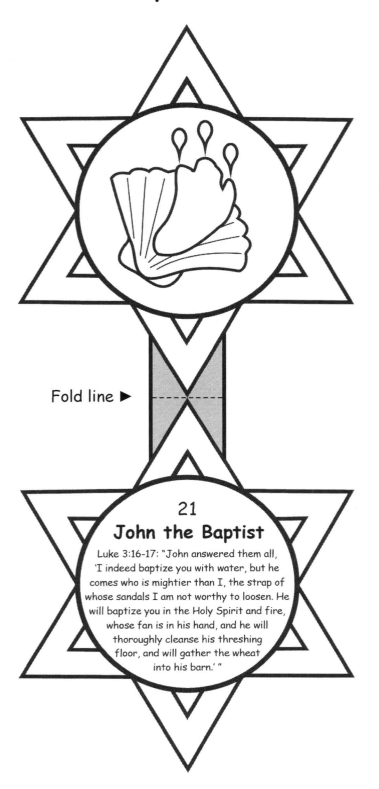

Fold line ▶

21
John the Baptist
Luke 3:16-17: "John answered them all,
'I indeed baptize you with water, but he
comes who is mightier than I, the strap of
whose sandals I am not worthy to loosen. He
will baptize you in the Holy Spirit and fire,
whose fan is in his hand, and he will
thoroughly cleanse his threshing
floor, and will gather the wheat
into his barn.' "

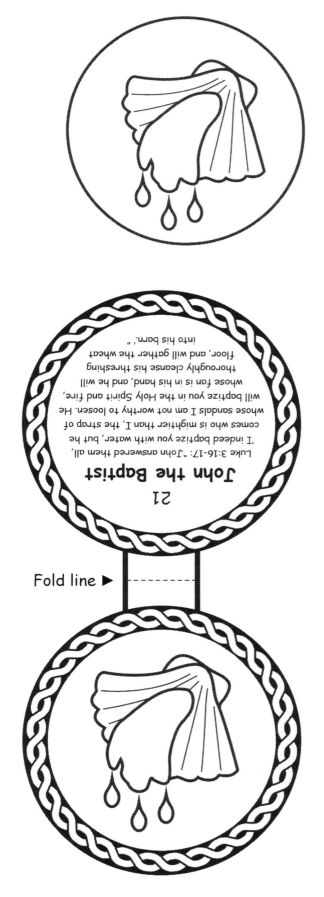

Fold line ▶

21
John the Baptist
Luke 3:16-17: "John answered them all,
'I indeed baptize you with water, but he
comes who is mightier than I, the strap of
whose sandals I am not worthy to loosen. He
will baptize you in the Holy Spirit and fire,
whose fan is in his hand, and he will
thoroughly cleanse his threshing
floor, and will gather the wheat
into his barn.' "

Ornaments for December 22: Bethlehem, the Birthplace of Jesus

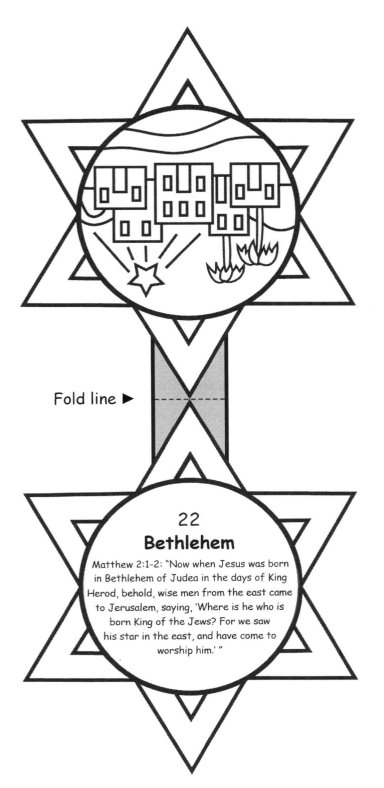

Fold line ▶

22
Bethlehem

Matthew 2:1-2: "Now when Jesus was born in Bethlehem of Judea in the days of King Herod, behold, wise men from the east came to Jerusalem, saying, 'Where is he who is born King of the Jews? For we saw his star in the east, and have come to worship him.' "

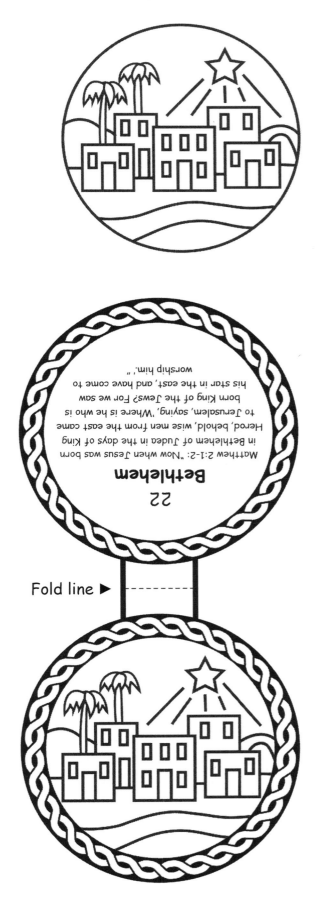

22
Bethlehem

Matthew 2:1-2: "Now when Jesus was born in Bethlehem of Judea in the days of King Herod, behold, wise men from the east came to Jerusalem, saying, 'Where is he who is born King of the Jews? For we saw his star in the east, and have come to worship him.' "

Fold line ▶

Ornaments for December 23: Angels proclaim the Birth of Jesus

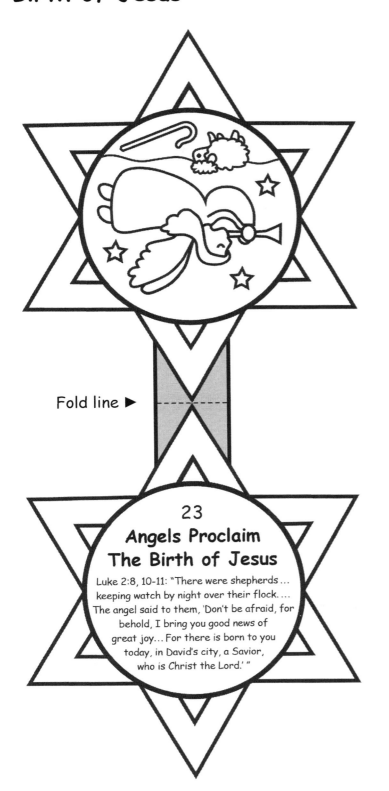

Fold line ▶

23
Angels Proclaim The Birth of Jesus

Luke 2:8, 10-11: "There were shepherds … keeping watch by night over their flock. … The angel said to them, 'Don't be afraid, for behold, I bring you good news of great joy… For there is born to you today, in David's city, a Savior, who is Christ the Lord.' "

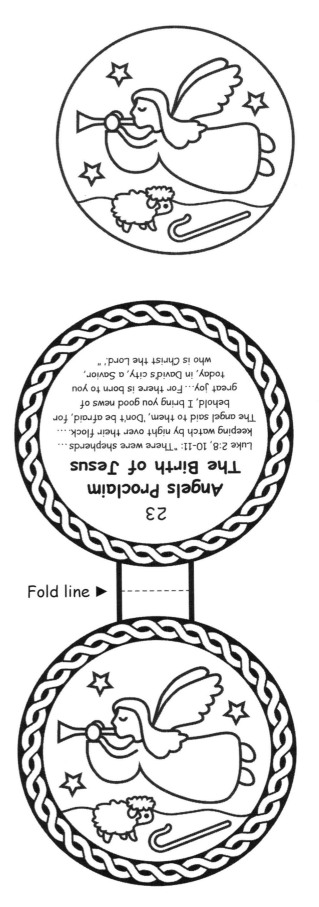

Fold line ▶

Ornaments for December 24: Birth of Jesus Christ on Christmas Day

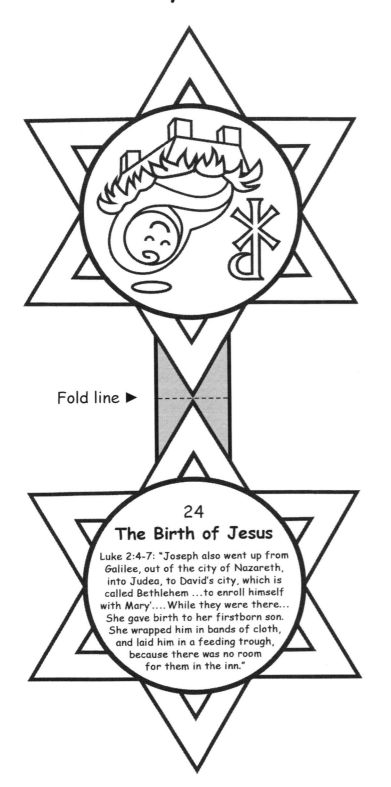

Fold line ▶ - - - - -

24
The Birth of Jesus

Luke 2:4-7: "Joseph also went up from Galilee, out of the city of Nazareth, into Judea, to David's city, which is called Bethlehem ...to enroll himself with Mary'.... While they were there... She gave birth to her firstborn son. She wrapped him in bands of cloth, and laid him in a feeding trough, because there was no room for them in the inn."

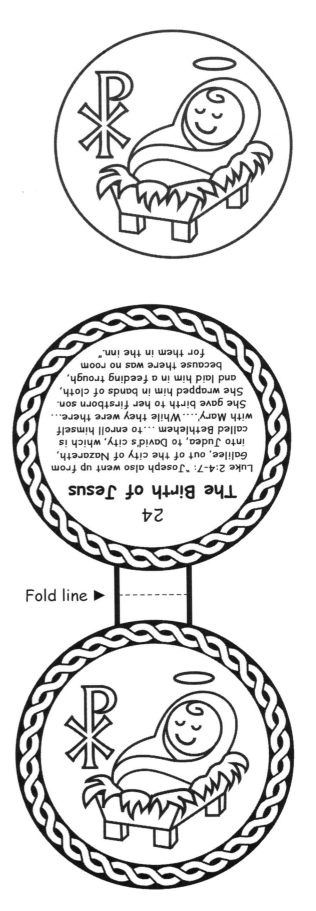

24
The Birth of Jesus

Luke 2:4-7: "Joseph also went up from Galilee, out of the city of Nazareth, into Judea, to David's city, which is called Bethlehem ...to enroll himself with Mary'.... While they were there... She gave birth to her firstborn son. She wrapped him in bands of cloth, and laid him in a feeding trough, because there was no room for them in the inn."

Fold line ▶ - - - - -

Instructions for Paper Jesse Tree

The pattern for this paper Jesse Tree is in 4 parts located on the next 4 pages. Paste, tape, or staple the 4 parts of the pattern together lining up the dashed lines for guides to make one single tree pattern. Then cut out 8 trees from the pattern using 12" x 18" colored construction paper or poster board. The tree is constructed by folding each tree piece lengthwise in half from top to bottom and then stapling, gluing, or taping (with double-sided tape) the backs of the folded 8 pieces together as shown below.

To the right is a top view of the tree showing 8 folded tree sections cut from the pattern with the backs together ready to glue, staple, or tape together. There will be no space between the pieces after they are fastened together.

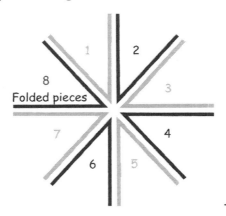

Below are examples of a completed tree with ornaments on it. Each tree vertical section of three branches is really two sheets of paper fastened together as shown above:

53

Pattern for Paper Jesse Tree

Part 1 of 4 parts

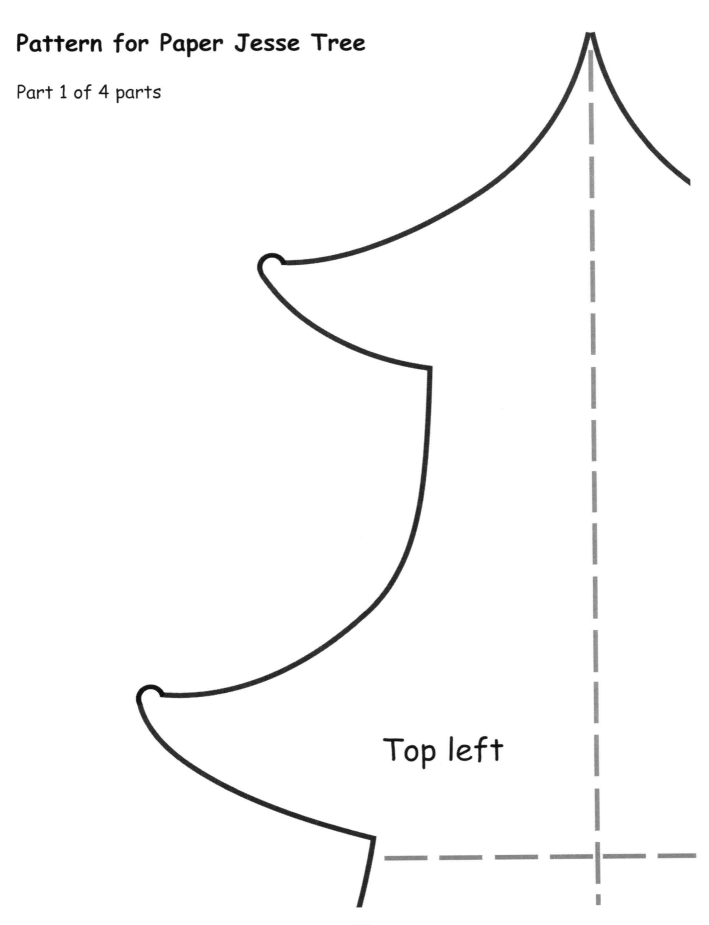

Top left

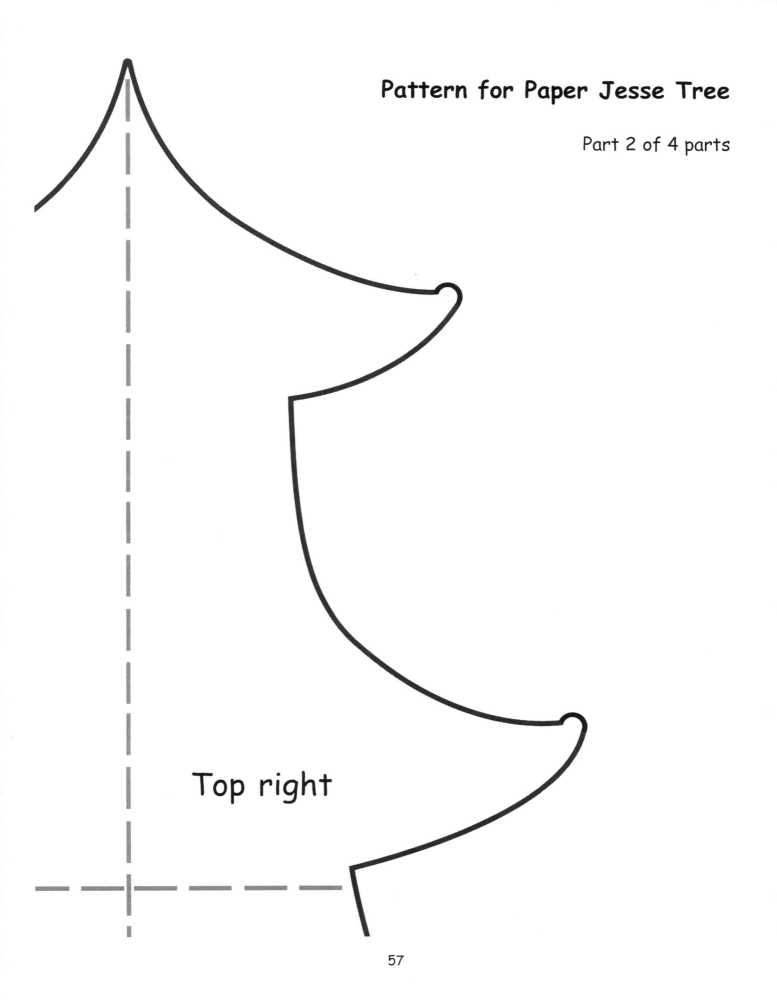

Pattern for Paper Jesse Tree

Top right

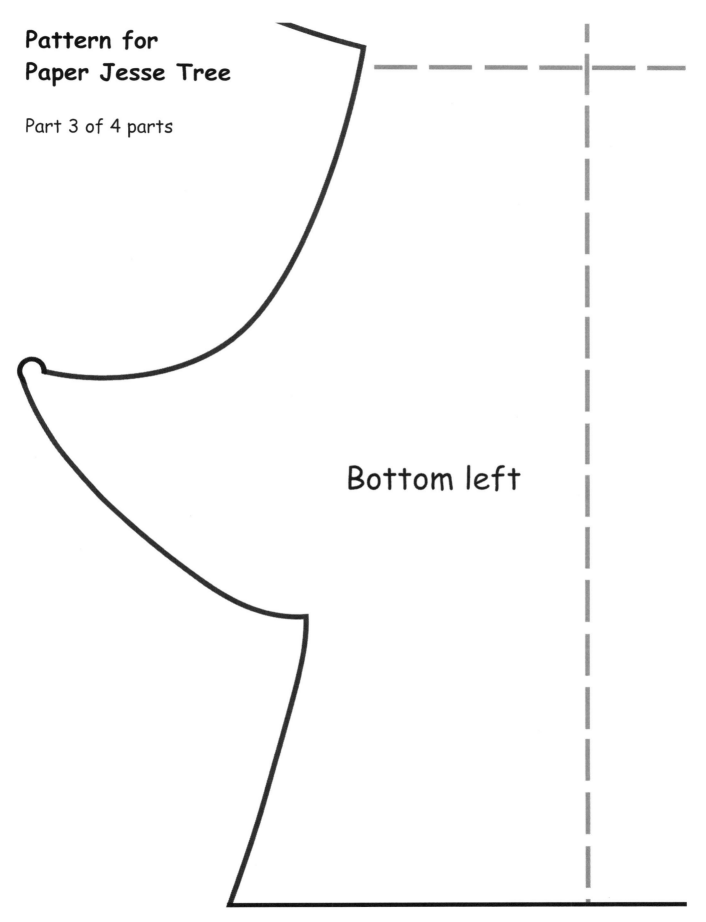

**Pattern for
Paper Jesse Tree**

Part 3 of 4 parts

Bottom left

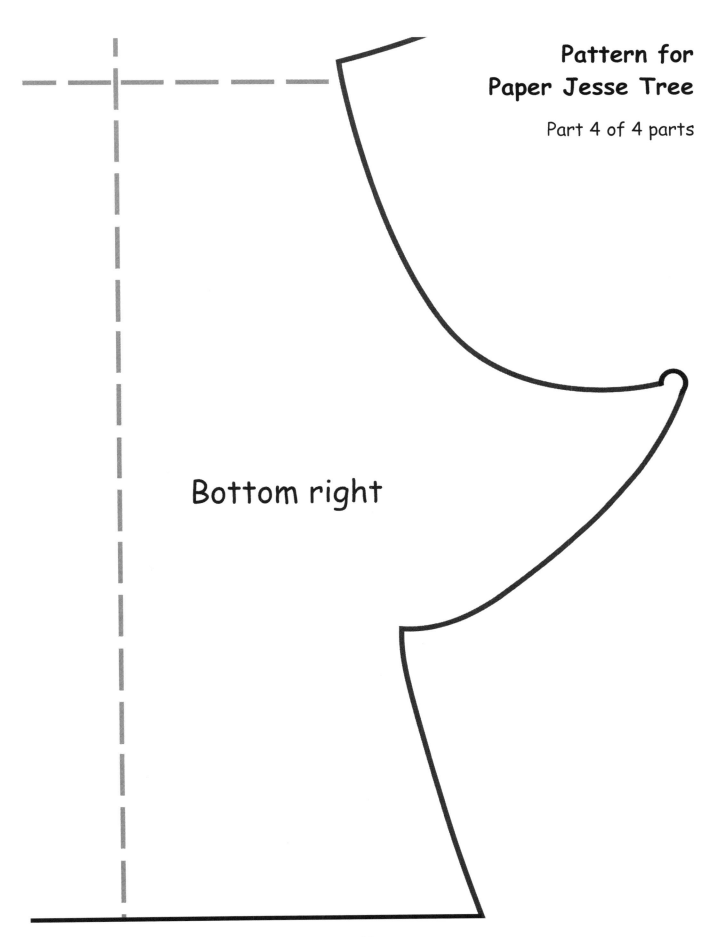

Bottom right

Optional Star for the Top of the Tree

If desired, a star can be made for the top of the tree using one of the patterns to the right. It can be colored or cut out from yellow construction paper and, if a single layer, laminated to make it more sturdy.

A star for use with paper tree made from the pattern in this book: Another option is to cut out 8 star pieces. Then fold each star in half from top to bottom as was done with the pieces from the paper tree pattern. Glue, staple, or tape the backs together on the top 3/4 of the star leaving the bottom 1/4 of the star free to set on top of the paper tree. Below is a top view of how the folded star pieces fit together for the 8-sided star.

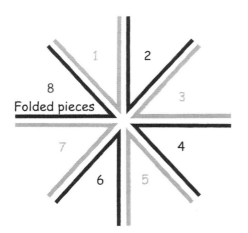

Folded pieces

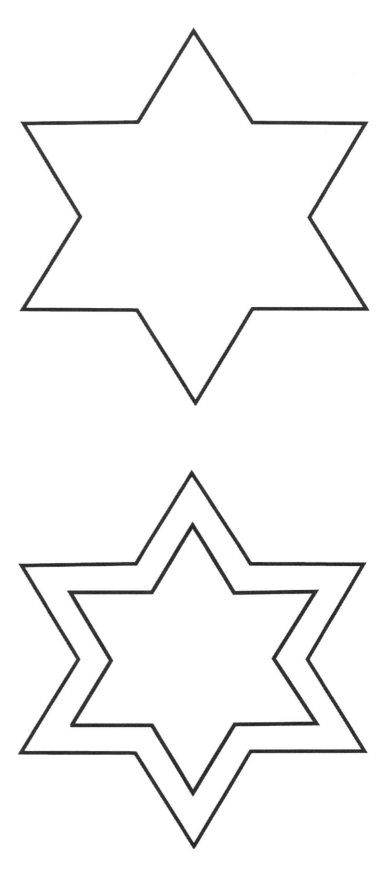

Bible Stories and Scripture Passages
for each Jesse Tree Ornament

The following pages accompany the ornaments and explain their meaning with
Bible stories and passages for different age groups and reading levels.

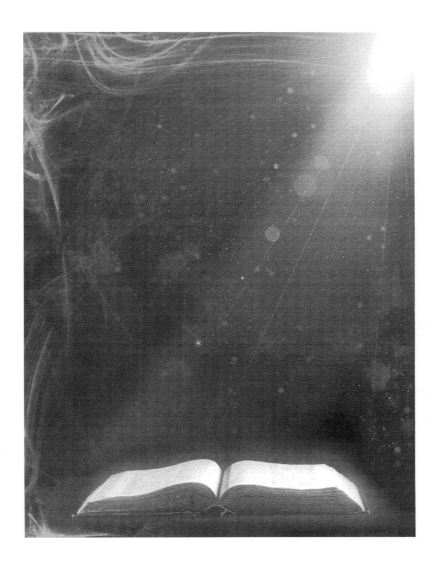

December 1: The Story of Creation

God created the heavens and the earth out of nothing and all that was on the earth in 6 days. He created light and darkness, waters and seas, dry land, plants, trees, insects, fish, birds, animals, and all the living creatures. Then God created man and woman. God saw everything he created and said it was good. God rested on the 7th day and blessed this day. God created the first man named Adam from the dust of the earth and breathed life into him. God placed Adam in a beautiful place called the Garden of Eden, also called Paradise. Then he created the first woman named Eve from a rib from Adam's side to be his wife and companion. Adam and Eve are the first parents of all the people in the world.

"The Creation of Adam" by Michelangelo, fresco on the ceiling of the Sistine Chapel, 1512

Genesis 1:1-31. [1] In the beginning, God created the heavens and the earth. [2] The earth was formless and empty. Darkness was on the surface of the deep and God's Spirit was hovering over the surface of the waters.

[3] God said, "Let there be light," and there was light. [4] God saw the light, and saw that it was good. God divided the light from the darkness.

[5] God called the light "day", and the darkness he called "night". There was evening and there was morning, the first day.

[6] God said, "Let there be an expanse in the middle of the waters, and let it divide the waters from the waters." [7] God made the expanse, and divided the waters which were under the expanse from the waters which were above the expanse; and it was so. [8] God called the expanse "sky".

There was evening and there was morning, a second day.

⁹ God said, "Let the waters under the sky be gathered together to one place, and let the dry land appear"; and it was so. ¹⁰ God called the dry land "earth", and the gathering together of the waters he called "seas". God saw that it was good. ¹¹ God said, "Let the earth yield grass, herbs yielding seeds, and fruit trees bearing fruit after their kind, with their seeds in it, on the earth"; and it was so. ¹² The earth yielded grass, herbs yielding seed after their kind, and trees bearing fruit, with their seeds in it, after their kind; and God saw that it was good. ¹³ There was evening and there was morning, a third day.

¹⁴ God said, "Let there be lights in the expanse of sky to divide the day from the night; and let them be for signs to mark seasons, days, and years; ¹⁵ and let them be for lights in the expanse of sky to give light on the earth"; and it was so. ¹⁶ God made the two great lights: the greater light to rule the day, and the lesser light to rule the night. He also made the stars. ¹⁷ God set them in the expanse of sky to give light to the earth, ¹⁸ and to rule over the day and over the night, and to divide the light from the darkness. God saw that it was good. ¹⁹ There was evening and there was morning, a fourth day.

²⁰ God said, "Let the waters abound with living creatures, and let birds fly above the earth in the open expanse of sky."

²¹ God created the large sea creatures and every living creature that moves, with which the waters swarmed, after their kind, and every winged bird after its kind. God saw that it was good.

²² God blessed them, saying, "Be fruitful, and multiply, and fill the waters in the seas, and let birds multiply on the earth." ²³ There was evening and there was morning, a fifth day.

²⁴ God said, "Let the earth produce living creatures after their kind, livestock, creeping things, and animals of the earth after their kind"; and it was so.

²⁵ God made the animals of the earth after their kind, and the livestock after their kind, and everything that creeps on the ground after its kind. God saw that it was good.

²⁶ God said, "Let us make man in our image, after our likeness: and let them have dominion over the fish of the sea, and over the birds of the

sky, and over the livestock, and over all the earth, and over every creeping thing that creeps on the earth." ²⁷ God created man in his own image. In God's image he created him; male and female he created them. ²⁸ God blessed them. God said to them, "Be fruitful, multiply, fill the earth, and subdue it. Have dominion over the fish of the sea, over the birds of the sky, and over every living thing that moves on the earth."

²⁹ God said, "Behold, I have given you every herb yielding seed, which is on the surface of all the earth, and every tree, which bears fruit yielding seed. It will be your food. ³⁰ To every animal of the earth, and to every bird of the sky, and to everything that creeps on the earth, in which there is life, I have given every green herb for food;" and it was so.

³¹ God saw everything that he had made, and, behold, it was very good. There was evening and there was morning, a sixth day.

Genesis 2:1-3, 7, 22. ¹ The heavens, the earth, and all their vast array were finished.

² On the seventh day God finished his work which he had done; and he rested on the seventh day from all his work which he had done.

³ God blessed the seventh day, and made it holy, because he rested in it from all his work of creation which he had done.

⁷ Yahweh God formed man from the dust of the ground, and breathed into his nostrils the breath of life;

²² Yahweh God made a woman from the rib which had taken from the man, and brought her to the man.

"The Garden of Eden"
Thomas Cole, c. 1828

December 2: The Fall of Adam and Eve

God told Adam and Eve they could eat of all the trees in the Garden of Eden except for one called the "Tree of the Knowledge of Good and Evil." The devil is a fallen angel who disobeyed God and lost Heaven. He hates God and people. He disguised himself as a snake (serpent) and tempted Eve to disobey God. She listened to him and ate the forbidden fruit. She gave some to Adam, and he ate it too. Because of their sin they lost some of God's wonderful blessings for all of mankind. They had to leave the Garden of Eden, and sickness and death entered the world. Their sin is called original sin, which means the first sin.

"Adam and Eve Driven out of Eden"
Gustave Doré, 1800s

Genesis 2:17. [17] "…but you shall not eat of the tree of the knowledge of good and evil; for in the day that you eat of it, you will surely die."

Genesis 3:1-20, 24. [1] Now the serpent was more subtle than any animal of the field which Yahweh God had made. He said to the woman, "Has God really said, 'You shall not eat of any tree of the garden?'"

[2] The woman said to the serpent, "We may eat fruit from the trees of the garden, [3] but not the fruit of the tree which is in the middle of the garden. God has said, 'You shall not eat of it. You shall not touch it, lest you die.'"

[4] The serpent said to the woman, "You won't surely die, [5] for God knows that in the day you eat it, your eyes will be opened, and you will be like God, knowing good and evil."

[6] When the woman saw that the tree was good for food, and that it was a delight to the eyes, and that the tree was to be desired to make one wise, she took some of its fruit, and ate; and she gave some to her husband with her, and he ate it, too. [7] Their eyes were opened, and they both knew that they were naked. They sewed fig leaves together, and made coverings for themselves. [8] They heard Yahweh God's voice walking in the garden in the cool of the day, and the man and his wife hid themselves from the presence of Yahweh God among the trees of the garden.

[9] Yahweh God called to the man, and said to him, "Where are you?"

[10] The man said, "I heard your voice in the garden, and I was afraid, because I was naked; and I hid myself."

[11] God said, "Who told you that you were naked? Have you eaten from the tree that I commanded you not to eat from?"

[12] The man said, "The woman whom you gave to be with me, she gave me fruit from the tree, and I ate it."

[13] Yahweh God said to the woman, "What have you done?"

The woman said, "The serpent deceived me, and I ate."

[14] Yahweh God said to the serpent, "Because you have done this, you are cursed above all livestock, and above every animal of the field. You shall go on your belly and you shall eat dust all the days of your life. [15] I will put hostility between you and the woman, and between your offspring and her offspring. He will bruise your head, and you will bruise his heel."

[16] To the woman he said, "I will greatly multiply your pain in childbirth. In pain you will bear children. Your desire will be for your husband, and he will rule over you."

[17] To Adam he said, "Because you have listened to your wife's voice, and ate from the tree, about which I commanded you, saying, 'You shall not eat of it,' the ground is cursed for your sake. You will eat from it with much labor all the days of your life. [18] It will yield thorns and thistles to you; and you will eat the herb of the field. [19] By the sweat of your face will you eat bread until you return to the ground, for out of it you were taken. For you are dust, and to dust you shall return."

[20] The man called his wife Eve because she would be the mother of all the living…. [24] So he drove out the man; and he placed cherubim at the east of the garden of Eden, and a flaming sword which turned every way, to guard the way to the tree of life.

December 3: Noah and the Ark

After a time sin in the world increased so much that almost everyone was wicked except for just a few people. Things got so bad that God decided to destroy all the people on the earth with a great flood, except for Noah and his family. God told Noah to build an ark and put a pair of each kind of animal in the ark along with his wife and children and their families. He told him to also bring food. In this way God saved Noah and his family from the great flood because Noah was a righteous man. After the flood, God made a rainbow in the sky. God said that the rainbow would be a sign that he would never destroy the whole world with a flood ever again. God blessed Noah and his family and told them to be fruitful and multiply.

"Noah's Ark", Edward Hicks, 1846

Genesis 6:11-22. [11] The earth was corrupt before God, and the earth was filled with violence. [12] God saw the earth, and saw that it was corrupt, for all flesh had corrupted their way on the earth.

[13] God said to Noah, "I will bring an end to all flesh, for the earth is filled with violence through them. Behold, I will destroy them and the earth. [14] Make a ship of gopher wood. You shall make rooms in the ship, and shall seal it inside and outside with pitch. [15] This is how you shall make it. The length of the ship shall be three hundred cubits, its width fifty cubits, and its height thirty cubits. [16] You shall make a roof in the ship, and you shall finish it to a cubit upward. You shall set the door of the ship in its side. You shall make it with lower, second, and third levels.

[17] I, even I, will bring the flood of waters on this earth, to destroy all flesh having the breath of life from under the sky. Everything that is in the earth will die. [18] But I will establish my covenant with you. You shall come into the ship, you, your sons, your wife, and your sons' wives with you. [19] Of every living thing of all flesh, you shall bring two of every sort into the ship, to keep them alive with you. They shall be male and female. [20] Of the birds after their kind, of the livestock after their kind, of every creeping thing of the ground after its kind, two of every sort will come to you, to keep them alive. [21] Take with you of all food that is eaten, and gather it to yourself; and it will be for food for you, and for them." [22] Thus Noah did. He did all that God commanded him.

Genesis 7:12, 23. [12] It rained on the earth forty days and forty nights…. [23] Every living thing was destroyed that was on the surface of the ground…. Only Noah was left, and those who were with him in the ship.

Genesis 9:1, 13-15. [1] God blessed Noah and his sons, and said to them, "Be fruitful, and multiply, and replenish the earth.

[13] I set my rainbow in the cloud, and it will be a sign of a covenant between me and the earth. [14] When I bring a cloud over the earth, that the rainbow will be seen in the cloud, [15] and I will remember my covenant, which is between me and you and every living creature of all flesh, and the waters will no more become a flood to destroy all flesh.

6:15 A cubit is the length from the tip of the middle finger to the elbow on a man's arm, or about 18 inches or 46 centimeters.

December 4: Abraham the Patriarch and Sarah his wife

Abram was born about ten generations after Noah lived. God told Abram to leave his country and relatives and go to a new land. God promised to make of him a great nation, make his name great, and bless him. When Abram was 99 years old, God gave Abram the new name of Abraham, which means "a father of many nations." God made a new covenant with Abraham. God also renamed his wife from Sarai to Sarah. God told Abraham that Sarah would have their firstborn son even though she was too old to have children. Not long afterwards some angels visited Abraham and told him that his son would be born by the next year. Sarah overheard this and laughed because she was about 90 years old and too old to have a baby. The angel asked Abraham why Sarah laughed because nothing is too hard for God to do. Sarah was frightened and denied laughing, even though she did laugh.

"The Vision of the Lord Directing Abram to Count the Stars", Julius Schnorr von Carolsfeld, 1860

Genesis 12:1-5, 7. [1] Now Yahweh said to Abram, "Leave your country, and your relatives, and your father's house, and go to the land that I will show you. [2] I will make of you a great nation. I will bless you and make your name great. You will be a blessing. [3] I will bless those who bless you, and I will curse him who curses you. All the families of the earth will be blessed through you." [4] So Abram went, as Yahweh had told him. Lot went with him. Abram was seventy-five years old when he departed from Haran. [5] Abram took Sarai his wife, Lot his brother's son, all their possessions that they had gathered, and the people whom they had acquired in Haran, and they went to go into the land of Canaan. They entered into the land of Canaan.... [7] Yahweh appeared to Abram and said, "I will give this land to your offspring."...

Genesis 15:5. Yahweh brought him outside, and said, "Look now toward the sky, and count the stars, if you are able to count them." He said to Abram, "So your offspring will be."...

Genesis 17:15-16. [15] God said to Abraham, "As for Sarai your wife, you shall not call her name Sarai, but her name will be Sarah. [16] I will bless her, and moreover I will give you a son by her. Yes, I will bless her, and she will be a mother of nations. Kings of peoples will come from her."

Genesis 18:11-15. [11] Now Abraham and Sarah were old, well advanced in age. Sarah had passed the age of childbearing. [12] Sarah laughed within herself, saying, "After I have grown old will I have pleasure, my lord being old also?" [13] Yahweh said to Abraham, "Why did Sarah laugh, saying, 'Will I really bear a child when I am old?' [14] Is anything too hard for Yahweh? At the set time I will return to you, when the season comes round, and Sarah will have a son." [15] Then Sarah denied it, saying, "I didn't laugh," for she was afraid. He said, "No, but you did laugh."

December 5: Isaac, son of Abraham

Isaac was born when Abraham was 100 years old as God had foretold. Isaac was the only son that Sarah and Abraham had together. Abraham loved Isaac very much, and Isaac was his only heir. God decided to test Abraham to see if he loved God more than anyone or anything else. God told Abraham to go to a mountain and to sacrifice his beloved son Isaac. Abraham obeyed God. He took Isaac to the mountain, built an altar, tied up Isaac, and put him on the altar. He drew his knife to kill him, but at that very moment an angel of God stopped him. The angel told him to sacrifice a ram instead that was stuck in some branches nearby. Abraham obeyed God. He put God first before everything else, and God blessed him and his descendants.

"Isaac embraces his father Abraham after the Binding of Isaac", early 1900s Bible illustration

Genesis 22:1-12. [1] After these things, God tested Abraham, and said to him, "Abraham!" He said, "Here I am."

[2] He said, "Now take your son, your only son, Isaac, whom you love, and go into the land of Moriah. Offer him there as a burnt offering on one of the mountains which I will tell you of."

[3] Abraham rose early in the morning, and saddled his donkey; and took two of his young men with him, and Isaac his son. He split the wood for the burnt offering, and rose up, and went to the place of which God had told him. [4] On the third day Abraham lifted up his eyes, and saw the place far off. [5] Abraham said to his young men, "Stay here with the donkey. The boy and I will go over there. We will worship, and come back to you." [6] Abraham took the wood of the burnt offering and laid it on Isaac his son. He took in his hand the fire and the knife. They both went together. [7] Isaac spoke to Abraham his father, and said, "My father?"

He said, "Here I am, my son."

He said, "Here is the fire and the wood, but where is the lamb for a burnt offering?"

[8] Abraham said, "God will provide himself the lamb for a burnt offering, my son." So they both went together. [9] They came to the place which God had told him of. Abraham built the altar there, and laid the wood in order, bound Isaac his son, and laid him on the altar, on the wood. [10] Abraham stretched out his hand, and took the knife to kill his son.

[11] Yahweh's angel called to him out of the sky, and said, "Abraham, Abraham!"

He said, "Here I am."

[12] He said, "Don't lay your hand on the boy or do anything to him. For now I know that you fear God, since you have not withheld your son, your only son, from me."

December 6: Jacob, son of Isaac

When Isaac was about 40 years old, he married Rebekah. They had twin boys named Esau and Jacob. Esau was born first, and in those days that meant because he was the oldest he would inherit the birthright from his father. When Isaac got old and blind, Rebekah and Jacob tricked Isaac into blessing Jacob with the inheritance of being the firstborn son. Later Jacob dreamed about a stairway going to Heaven with angels going up and down. God told Jacob that he would have many descendants, and that he would give him a land for him and his offspring. Jacob is also called Israel. He became the father of twelve sons from whom descended the twelve tribes of Israel. This is how the Jewish nation began.

"Jacob's Ladder" by William Blake
c. 1800, British Museum, London

Genesis 25:20, 24-26.
[20] Isaac was forty years old when he took Rebekah, the daughter of Bethuel the Syrian of Paddan Aram, the sister of Laban the Syrian, to be his wife....
[24] When her days to be delivered were fulfilled, behold, there were twins in her womb. [25] The first came out red all over, like a hairy garment. They named him Esau. [26] After that, his brother came out, and his hand had hold on Esau's heel. He was named Jacob.....

Genesis 27:35-36. [35] He said, "Your brother came with deceit, and has taken away your blessing." [36] He said, "Isn't he rightly named Jacob? For he has supplanted me these two times. He took away my birthright. See, now he has taken away my blessing." He said, "Haven't you reserved a blessing for me?"...

Genesis 28:10-17. [10] Jacob went out from Beersheba, and went toward Haran. [11] He came to a certain place, and stayed there all night, because the sun had set. He took one of the stones of the place, and put it under his head, and lay down in that place to sleep. [12] He dreamed and saw a stairway set upon the earth, and its top reached to heaven. Behold, the angels of God were ascending and descending on it. [13] Behold, Yahweh stood above it, and said, "I am Yahweh, the God of Abraham your father, and the God of Isaac. I will give the land you lie on to you and to your offspring. [14] Your offspring will be as the dust of the earth, and you will spread abroad to the west, and to the east, and to the north, and to the south. In you and in your offspring, all the families of the will earth be blessed. [15] Behold, I am with you, and will keep you, wherever you go, and will bring you again into this land. For I will not leave you, until I have done that which I have spoken of to you."
[16] Jacob awakened out of his sleep, and he said, "Surely Yahweh is in this place, and I didn't know it." [17] He was afraid, and said, "How awesome this place is! This is none other than God's house, and this is the gate of heaven."

Genesis 32:27-28. [27] He said to him, "What is your name?" He said, "Jacob". [28] He said, "Your name will no longer be called Jacob, but Israel; for you have fought with God and with men, and have prevailed."

Genesis 35:11-12. [11] God said to him, "I am God Almighty. Be fruitful and multiply. A nation and a company of nations will be from you, and kings will come out of your body. [12] The land which I gave to Abraham and Isaac, I will give it to you, and to your offspring after you will I give the land."

December 7: Joseph, son of Jacob

One of Jacob's twelve sons was named Joseph. Jacob loved Joseph very much because he was the son of his old age. He made him a special coat of many colors. It made his brothers so jealous that Jacob was Joseph's favorite son that they sold him into slavery in Egypt. However, this turned out to be for the best because Joseph eventually became a ruler in Egypt. Later Pharaoh, the king of Egypt, had a dream that he didn't understand. Joseph interpreted the dream to mean that there would be a severe famine. Then Joseph told Pharaoh how to help his people. He told him to store up food during the next seven prosperous years so that the people would have food during the following seven years of famine. Back at home, Jacob and his family were suffering from the lack of food. They heard there was food in Egypt so Jacob sent some his sons to Egypt to buy food. Joseph forgave his brothers, and the family eventually all went to live in Egypt with Joseph during the famine. That is how the Israelites came to live in Egypt.

"Joseph and His Brethren Welcomed by Pharaoh"
James Tissot, c. 1900

Genesis 37:1-4, 24, 28. [1] Jacob lived in the land of his father's travels, in the land of Canaan. [2] This is the history of the generations of Jacob. Joseph, being seventeen years old, was feeding the flock with his brothers. He was a boy with the sons of Bilhah and Zilpah, his father's wives. Joseph brought an evil report of them to their father. [3] Now Israel loved Joseph more than all his children, because he was the son of his old age, and he made him a coat of many colors. [4] His brothers saw that their father loved him more than all his brothers, and they hated him, and couldn't speak peaceably to him....

[24] ...and they took him, and threw him into the pit. The pit was empty. There was no water in it.... [28] Midianites who were merchants passed by, and they drew and lifted up Joseph out of the pit, and sold Joseph to the Ishmaelites for twenty pieces of silver. They brought Joseph into Egypt....

Genesis 41:15-16, 28-30, 40. [15] Pharaoh said to Joseph, "I have dreamed a dream, and there is no one who can interpret it. I have heard it said of you, that when you hear a dream you can interpret it." [16] Joseph answered Pharaoh, saying, "It isn't in me. God will give Pharaoh an answer of peace."...

[28] That is the thing which I have spoken to Pharaoh. God has shown Pharaoh what he is about to do. [29] Behold, seven years of great plenty throughout all the land of Egypt are coming. [30] Seven years of famine will arise after them, and all the plenty will be forgotten in the land of Egypt...

[40] You shall be over my house, and according to your word will all my people be ruled. Only in the throne I will be greater than you."

December 8: Moses and the Passover

The Israelites were slaves to Pharaoh. Because they were growing in number, Pharaoh was afraid that they would no longer obey him so he ordered all the male babies killed. To save baby Moses his mother hid him in a basket on the river. The daughter of Pharaoh found him and raised him like her own child. When Moses grew up, God told him to lead the Israelites out of Egypt to the Promised Land; however, Pharaoh didn't want to let them go. God ended up sending 10 plagues to convince Pharaoh. The 10th plague was the worst, the death of all the firstborn in the land of Egypt. During this last plague God told the Israelites to mark the doors of their houses with the blood of a lamb to be a sign for the plague to *pass over* their houses. When Pharaoh's son was killed, he finally let the Israelites go. During the Passover celebration each year Jews remember how God rescued them from slavery in Egypt, how quickly they left, and how there wasn't even enough time to let the bread dough rise before baking it. That is why only unleavened bread is eaten for the Feast of the Unleavened Bread.

"Moses rescued from the Nile"
Nicolas Poussin, 1638

Exodus 2:5-10. [5] Pharaoh's daughter came down to bathe at the river. Her maidens walked along by the riverside. She saw the basket among the reeds, and sent her servant to get it. [6] She opened it, and saw the child, and behold, the baby cried. She had compassion on him, and said, "This is one of the Hebrews' children.

[7] Then his sister said to Pharaoh's daughter, "Should I go and call a nurse for you from the Hebrew

women, that she may nurse the child for you?" [8] Pharaoh's daughter said to her, "Go." The young woman went and called the child's mother.

[9] Pharaoh's daughter said to her, "Take this child away, and nurse him for me, and I will give you your wages." The woman took the child, and nursed it. [10] The child grew, and she brought him to Pharaoh's daughter, and he became her son. She named him Moses, and said, "Because I drew him out of the water."

Exodus 12:3, 5-8, 11-15. [3] Speak to all the congregation of Israel, saying, 'On the tenth day of this month, they shall take to them every man a lamb, according to their fathers' houses, a lamb for a household... [5] Your lamb shall be without defect, a male a year old....[6] You shall keep it until the fourteenth day of the same month; and the whole assembly of the congregation of Israel shall kill it at evening. [7] They shall take some of the blood, and put it on the two door posts and on the lintel, on the houses in which they shall eat it. [8] They shall eat the meat in that night, roasted with fire, and unleavened bread. They shall eat it with bitter herbs....

[11] This is how you shall eat it: with your belt on your waist, your shoes on your feet, and your staff in your hand; and you shall eat it in haste: it is Yahweh's Passover. [12] For I will go through the land of Egypt in that night, and will strike all the firstborn in the land of Egypt, both man and animal. I will execute judgments against all the gods of Egypt. I am Yahweh. [13] The blood shall be to you for a token on the houses where you are. When I see the blood, I will pass over you, and no plague will be on you to destroy you when I strike the land of Egypt. [14] This day shall be a memorial for you. You shall keep it as a feast to Yahweh. You shall keep it as a feast throughout your generations by an ordinance forever. [15] "Seven days you shall eat unleavened bread; even the first day you shall put away yeast out of your houses, for whoever eats leavened bread from the first day until the seventh day, that soul shall be cut off from Israel."

December 9: Moses and the Ten Commandments

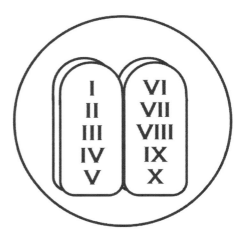

After the 10th plague, Moses was able to lead his people out of Egypt. This is called "The Exodus". After they left Pharaoh changed his mind about letting the Israelites go and took his army to try to recapture them. When Moses and the people came to the Red Sea, God worked a miracle; God parted the sea so that the Israelites could walk through and escape the Egyptians. When the Egyptians followed them, the sea fell back on them. The Israelites escaped Pharaoh and wandered in the desert for 40 years. During that time Moses went up Mt. Sinai where God gave him the 10 commandments inscribed on two stone tablets. The first three commandments are about how to love God above all things, and the last seven commandments are about how to love other people.

"Moses Receiving the Law"
William Blake, 1780

Exodus 14:13-16. [13] Moses said to the people, "Don't be afraid. Stand still, and see the salvation of Yahweh, which he will work for you today; for you will never again see the Egyptians whom you have seen today. [14] Yahweh will fight for you, and you shall be still."

[15] Yahweh said to Moses, "Why do you cry to me? Speak to the children of Israel, that they go forward. [16] Lift up your rod, and stretch out your hand over the sea and divide it. Then the children of Israel shall go into the middle of the sea on dry ground."

Exodus 20:1-17. [1] God spoke all these words, saying, [2] "I am Yahweh your God, who brought you out of the land of Egypt, out of the house of bondage. [3] "You shall have no other gods before me. [4] "You shall not make for yourselves an idol, nor any image of anything that is in the heavens above, or that is in the earth beneath, or that is in the water under the earth: [5] you shall not bow yourself down to them, nor serve them, for I, Yahweh your God, am a jealous God, visiting the iniquity of the fathers on the children, on the third and on the fourth generation of those who hate me, [6] and showing loving kindness to thousands of those who love me and keep my commandments. [7] "You shall not take the name of Yahweh your God in vain, for Yahweh will not hold him guiltless who takes his name in vain. [8] "Remember the Sabbath day, to keep it holy. [9] You shall labor six days, and do all your work, [10] but the seventh day is a Sabbath to Yahweh your God. You shall not do any work in it, you, nor your son, nor your daughter, your male servant, nor your female servant, nor your livestock, nor your stranger who is within your gates; [11] for in six days Yahweh made heaven and earth, the sea, and all that is in them, and rested the seventh day; therefore Yahweh blessed the Sabbath day, and made it holy.

[12] "Honor your father and your mother, that your days may be long in the land which Yahweh your God gives you. [13] "You shall not murder. [14] "You shall not commit adultery. [15] "You shall not steal. [16] "You shall not give false testimony against your neighbor. [17] "You shall not covet your neighbor's house. You shall not covet your neighbor's wife, nor his male servant, nor his female servant, nor his ox, nor his donkey, nor anything that is your neighbor's."

December 10: Ruth and Boaz

Boaz was a wealthy landowner of Bethlehem. One day he noticed Ruth gathering leftover grain from his fields. It was the custom in those days that the poor could gather the grain left behind after the harvest. Boaz learned that Ruth had a hard life, and he invited her to eat with him and his workers. Boaz later married Ruth. They had a son named Obed who became the father of Jesse and grandfather of King David, an ancestor of Jesus.

"Ruth in Boaz's Field"
Julius Schnorr von Carolsfeld, 1828

Ruth 1:16-17. [16] Ruth said, "Don't urge me to leave you, and to return from following you, for where you go, I will go; and where you stay, I will stay. Your people will be my people, and your God my God. [17] Where you die, I will die, and there I will be buried. May Yahweh do so to me, and more also, if anything but death parts you and me."

Ruth 2:2-12. [2] Ruth the Moabitess said to Naomi, "Let me now go to the field, and glean among the ears of grain after him in whose sight I find favor."
She said to her, "Go, my daughter." [3] She went, and came and gleaned in the field after the reapers; and she happened to come to the portion of the field belonging to Boaz, who was of the family of Elimelech.

[4] Behold, Boaz came from Bethlehem, and said to the reapers, "May Yahweh be with you." They answered him, "May Yahweh bless you."
[5] Then Boaz said to his servant who was set over the reapers, "Whose young lady is this?"
[6] The servant who was set over the reapers answered, "It is the Moabite lady who came back with Naomi out of the country of Moab.
[7] She said, 'Please let me glean and gather after the reapers among the sheaves.' So she came, and has continued even from the morning until now, except that she rested a little in the house."
[8] Then Boaz said to Ruth, "Listen, my daughter. Don't go to glean in another field, and don't go from here, but stay here close to my maidens. [9] Let your eyes be on the field that they reap, and go after them. Haven't I commanded the young men not to touch you? When you are thirsty, go to the vessels, and drink from that which the young men have drawn."
[10] Then she fell on her face, and bowed herself to the ground, and said to him, "Why have I found favor in your sight, that you should take knowledge of me, since I am a foreigner?"
[11] Boaz answered her, "I have been fully told about all that you have done to your mother-in-law since the death of your husband, and how you have left your father and your mother, and the land of your birth, and have come to a people that you didn't know before.
[12] May Yahweh repay your work, and a full reward be given to you from Yahweh, the God of Israel, under whose wings you have come to take refuge."

Ruth 4:13-14. [13] So Boaz took Ruth, and she became his wife; and he went in to her, and Yahweh enabled her to conceive, and she bore a son. [14] The women said to Naomi, "Blessed be Yahweh, who has not left you today without a near kinsman. Let his name be famous in Israel...."

December 11: Samuel the Prophet

There was a woman named Hannah who was very sad that she didn't have any children. She prayed for a child and promised that she would dedicate the child to God. Later she had a son named Samuel, which means "God has heard" or "asked of God." Samuel went to live with the priest Eli at an early age. One night Samuel lay down in the temple. It was getting dark but God's lamp had not gone out. Samuel heard a voice calling his name. He thought it was Eli, but Eli told him to go back to sleep. After this happened three times, Eli realized that the voice was the Lord calling Samuel so Eli instructed Samuel to answer, "Speak, Lord, your servant is listening." Samuel became a great prophet who helped keep Israel's religious heritage of the alive.

"The Infant Samuel"
Sir Joshua Reynolds, 1700s

 1 Samuel 1:11, 20.
¹¹She vowed a vow, and said, "Yahweh of Armies, if you will indeed look at the affliction of your servant, and remember me, and not forget your servant, but will give to your servant a boy, then I will give him to Yahweh all the days of his life, and no razor shall come on his head."...
²⁰When the time had come, Hannah conceived, and bore a son; and she named him Samuel, saying, "Because I have asked him of Yahweh."

1 Samuel 3:1-20. ¹The child Samuel ministered to Yahweh before Eli. Yahweh's word was rare in those days. There were not many visions, then. ²At that time, when Eli was laid down in his place (now his eyes had begun to grow dim, so that he could not see), ³and God's lamp hadn't yet gone out, and Samuel had laid down in Yahweh's temple, where God's ark was; ⁴Yahweh called Samuel; and he said, "Here I am."

⁵He ran to Eli, and said, "Here I am; for you called me." He said, "I didn't call. Lie down again." He went and lay down. ⁶Yahweh called yet again, "Samuel!" Samuel arose and went to Eli, and said, "Here I am; for you called me." He answered, "I didn't call, my son. Lie down again." ⁷Now Samuel didn't yet know Yahweh, neither was Yahweh's word yet revealed to him.

⁸Yahweh called Samuel again the third time. He arose and went to Eli, and said, "Here I am; for you called me." Eli perceived that Yahweh had called the child. ⁹Therefore Eli said to Samuel, "Go, lie down. It shall be, if he calls you, that you shall say, 'Speak, Yahweh; for your servant hears.'" So Samuel went and lay down in his place. ¹⁰Yahweh came, and stood, and called as at other times, "Samuel! Samuel!" Then Samuel said, "Speak; for your servant hears."

¹¹Yahweh said to Samuel, "Behold, I will do a thing in Israel, at which both the ears of everyone who hears it will tingle. ¹²In that day I will perform against Eli all that I have spoken concerning his house, from the beginning even to the end. ¹³For I have told him that I will judge his house forever, for the iniquity which he knew, because his sons brought a curse on themselves, and he didn't restrain them. ¹⁴Therefore I have sworn to the house of Eli, that the iniquity of Eli's house shall not be removed with sacrifice or offering forever."

¹⁵Samuel lay until the morning, and opened the doors of Yahweh's house. Samuel feared to show Eli the vision. ¹⁶Then Eli called Samuel, and said, "Samuel, my son!" He said, "Here I am." ¹⁷He said, "What is the thing that he has spoken to you? Please don't hide it from me. God do so to you, and more also, if you hide anything from me of all the things that he spoke to you."

¹⁸Samuel told him every bit, and hid nothing from him. He said, "It is Yahweh. Let him do what seems good to him."

¹⁹Samuel grew, and Yahweh was with him, and let none of his words fall to the ground. ²⁰All Israel from Dan even to Beersheba knew that Samuel was established to be a prophet of Yahweh.

December 12: Branch of Jesse

The Israelites did not have a king to rule them, and they insisted on having a king. Samuel, the prophet, heard God tell him to anoint Saul as their first king so he did. However after Saul was king for many years, Saul disobeyed God's commands and lost God's favor. Samuel then sought a king from among the sons of Jesse of Bethlehem. Samuel examined seven of Jesse's sons and determined that "The Lord has not chosen these." He asked Jesse if he had another son. Jesse said that David, his youngest son, was tending the sheep. Samuel asked for David. When he came the Lord said to Samuel, "Rise and anoint him, this is the one." Samuel anointed him without Saul knowing, and later David did become the king of Israel. David is like a branch from the family tree of Jesse.

Tree of Jesse, Beauvais Cathedral

1 Samuel 13:13-14. [13]Samuel said to Saul, "You have done foolishly. You have not kept the commandment of Yahweh your God, which he commanded you; for now Yahweh would have established your kingdom on Israel forever. [14]But now your kingdom will not continue. Yahweh has sought for himself a man after his own heart, and Yahweh has appointed him to be prince over his people, because you have not kept that which Yahweh commanded you."

Isaiah 11:1-9. [1]A shoot will come out of the stock of Jesse, and a branch out of his roots will bear fruit.

[2]Yahweh's Spirit will rest on him: the spirit of wisdom and understanding, the spirit of counsel and might, the spirit of knowledge and of the fear of Yahweh.

[3]His delight will be in the fear of Yahweh. He will not judge by the sight of his eyes, neither decide by the hearing of his ears; [4]but with righteousness he will judge the poor, and decide with equity for the humble of the earth. He will strike the earth with the rod of his mouth; and with the breath of his lips he will kill the wicked.

[5]Righteousness will be the belt of his waist, and faithfulness the belt of his waist.

[6]The wolf will live with the lamb, and the leopard will lie down with the young goat; The calf, the young lion, and the fattened calf together; and a little child will lead them. [7]The cow and the bear will graze. Their young ones will lie down together. The lion will eat straw like the ox.

[8]The nursing child will play near a cobra's hole, and the weaned child will put his hand on the viper's den.

[9]They will not hurt nor destroy in all my holy mountain; for the earth will be full of the knowledge of Yahweh, as the waters cover the sea.

December 13: King David

King Saul was tormented by an evil spirit and became depressed. He sent for David who played the harp very well. When David played music for him, he would feel better, and the evil spirit would leave him. David wrote many songs now called Psalms, which are in the Bible. David also is known for being brave and killing the Philistine giant Goliath by using a rock and a slingshot. Later King Saul was killed in a battle with the Philistines. David was anointed king by the elders of Israel. The prophet Nathan announced to David that his "throne will be established forever." This was fulfilled in that Jesus Christ, the Messiah, is a descendent from the line of King David.

Statue of King David
by Nicolas Cordier

2 Samuel 7:16-17.
[16] "Your throne will be established forever."
[17] Nathan spoke to David...

1 Samuel 16:14-23. [14] Now Yahweh's Spirit departed from Saul, and an evil spirit from Yahweh troubled him. [15] Saul's servants said to him, "See now, an evil spirit from God troubles you. [16] Let our lord now command your servants who are in front of you to seek out a man who is a skillful player on the harp. Then when the evil spirit from God is on you, he will play with his hand, and you will be well."

[17] Saul said to his servants, "Provide me now a man who can play well, and bring him to me."

[18] Then one of the young men answered, and said, "Behold, I have seen a son of Jesse the Bethlehemite who is skillful in playing, a mighty man of valor, a man of war, prudent in speech, and a handsome person; and Yahweh is with him." [19] Therefore Saul sent messengers to Jesse, and said, "Send me David your son, who is with the sheep."

[20] Jesse took a donkey loaded with bread, and a bottle of wine, and a young goat, and sent them by David his son to Saul. [21] David came to Saul, and stood before him. He loved him greatly; and he became his armor bearer.

[22] Saul sent to Jesse, saying, "Please let David stand before me; for he has found favor in my sight." [23] When the spirit from God was on Saul, David took the harp, and played with his hand; so Saul was refreshed, and was well, and the evil spirit departed from him.

1 Samuel 17:49-50. [49] David put his hand in his bag, took a stone, and slung it, and struck the Philistine in his forehead. The stone sank into his forehead, and he fell on his face to the earth. [50] So David prevailed over the Philistine with a sling and with a stone, and struck the Philistine, and killed him; but there was no sword in the hand of David.

79

December 14: King Solomon

King Solomon was the second child of King David and Bathsheba. He had a dream one night that God told him to ask for whatever he wanted and God would give it to him. Solomon asked for wisdom to discern between good and bad in order to judge the people correctly. God was pleased with his prayer and gave him great wisdom. Unfortunately when Solomon grew older he took wives who worshipped false gods and was led astray by them even though the Lord appeared to him twice to warn him. Solomon disobeyed God and broke the covenant with him.

Because of this God said that he would tear apart the kingdom of Israel and leave only one tribe to his son for the sake of David his father and for the sake of Jerusalem.

"Dream of Solomon – God promises Solomon Wisdom", Luca Giordano, 1693

1 Kings 3:5-14. [5] In Gibeon, Yahweh appeared to Solomon in a dream by night; and God said, "Ask for what I should give you."

[6] Solomon said, "You have shown to your servant David my father great loving kindness, because he walked before you in truth, in righteousness, and in uprightness of heart with you. You have kept for him this great loving kindness, that you have given him a son to sit on his throne, as it is today.

[7] Now, Yahweh my God, you have made your servant king instead of David my father. I am just a little child. I don't know how to go out or come in. [8] Your servant is among your people which you have chosen, a great people, that can't be numbered or counted for multitude. [9] Give your servant therefore an understanding heart to judge your people, that I may discern between good and evil; for who is able to judge this great people of yours?"

[10] This request pleased the Lord, that Solomon had asked this thing. [11] God said to him, "Because you have asked this thing, and have not asked for yourself long life, nor have you asked for riches for yourself, nor have you asked for the life of your enemies, but have asked for yourself understanding to discern justice; [12] behold, I have done according to your word. Behold, I have given you a wise and understanding heart; so that there has been no one like you before you, and after you none will arise like you. [13] I have also given you that which you have not asked, both riches and honor, so that there will not be any among the kings like you for all your days.

[14] If you will walk in my ways, to keep my statutes and my commandments, as your father David walked, then I will lengthen your days."

I Kings 11:4, 9-13. [4] When Solomon was old, his wives turned away his heart after other gods; and his heart was not perfect with Yahweh his God, as the heart of David his father was.... [9] Yahweh was angry with Solomon, because his heart was turned away from Yahweh, the God of Israel, who had appeared to him twice, [10] and had commanded him concerning this thing, that he should not go after other gods; but he didn't keep that which Yahweh commanded. [11] Therefore Yahweh said to Solomon, "Because this is done by you, and you have not kept my covenant and my statutes, which I have commanded you, I will surely tear the kingdom from you, and will give it to your servant. [12] Nevertheless, I will not do it in your days, for David your father's sake; but I will tear it out of your son's hand. [13] However I will not tear away all the kingdom; but I will give one tribe to your son, for David my servant's sake, and for Jerusalem's sake which I have chosen."

December 15: Elijah the Prophet

Elijah was a great prophet, and God worked many miracles through him. One of the miracles happened on Mount Carmel during a famine. The king at that time and many of the people were worshipping Baal, a false god. Elijah proposed a test to see who was the most powerful, Baal or God (Yahweh). The people of Israel, 450 prophets of Baal, and 400 prophets of Asherah were summoned to Mount Carmel. Two altars were built, one for Baal and one for Yahweh. Wood was put on the altars and oxen were killed, cut into pieces, and laid on the wood. Elijah invited the priests of Baal to pray for fire to light the sacrifice; they prayed all morning with no success. Elijah made fun of them, but they cut themselves and added their own blood to the sacrifices and kept praying to the false god Baal with no success again. Then Elijah had his altar covered with water from four large jars to make it even harder to catch fire. He prayed to God to accept the sacrifice, and then fire fell from the sky consuming the water, the sacrifice, and even the stones of the altar. Elijah showed that God was real and Baal was not real by a miracle that only the one true God could do. Elijah ordered the deaths of the prophets of Baal. Then he prayed for rain because there was a drought for many years. Rain began that ended the drought and the famine.

"Elijah Begging for Fire from Heaven"
Master of James IV of Scotland, c. 1500

1 Kings 18:17-46. [17] When Ahab saw Elijah, Ahab said to him, "Is that you, you troubler of Israel?"

[18] He answered, "I have not troubled Israel; but you, and your father's house, in that you have forsaken Yahweh's commandments, and you have followed the Baals. [19] Now therefore send, and gather to me all Israel to Mount Carmel, and four hundred fifty of the prophets of Baal, and four hundred of the prophets of the Asherah, who eat at Jezebel's table."

[20] So Ahab sent to all the children of Israel, and gathered the prophets together to Mount Carmel. [21] Elijah came near to all the people, and said, "How long will you waver between the two sides? If Yahweh is God, follow him; but if Baal, then follow him." The people didn't say a word. [22] Then Elijah said to the people, "I, even I only, am left as a prophet of Yahweh; but Baal's prophets are four hundred fifty men. [23] Let them therefore give us two bulls; and let them choose one bull for themselves, and cut it in pieces, and lay it on the wood, and put no fire under; and I will dress the

other bull, and lay it on the wood, and put no fire under it. ²⁴ You call on the name of your god, and I will call on Yahweh's name. The God who answers by fire, let him be God."

All the people answered, "What you say is good." ²⁵ Elijah said to the prophets of Baal, "Choose one bull for yourselves, and dress it first; for you are many; and call on the name of your god, but put no fire under it."

²⁶ They took the bull which was given them, and they dressed it, and called on the name of Baal from morning even until noon, saying, "Baal, hear us!" But there was no voice, and nobody answered. They leaped about the altar which was made. ²⁷ At noon, Elijah mocked them, and said, "Cry aloud; for he is a god. Either he is deep in thought, or he has gone somewhere, or he is on a journey, or perhaps he sleeps and must be awakened."

²⁸ They cried aloud, and cut themselves in their way with knives and lances, until the blood gushed out on them. ²⁹ When midday was past, they prophesied until the time of the evening offering; but there was no voice, no answer, and nobody paid attention.

³⁰ Elijah said to all the people, "Come near to me!"; and all the people came near to him. He repaired the altar of Yahweh that had been thrown down.

³¹ Elijah took twelve stones, according to the number of the tribes of the sons of Jacob, to whom Yahweh's word came, saying, "Israel shall be your name."

³² With the stones he built an altar in Yahweh's name. He made a trench around the altar, large enough to contain two seahs of seed. ³³ He put the wood in order, and cut the bull in pieces, and laid it on the wood. He said, "Fill four jars with water, and pour it on the burnt offering, and on the wood."

³⁴ He said, "Do it a second time"; and they did it the second time. He said, "Do it a third time"; and they did it the third time. ³⁵ The water ran around the altar; and he also filled the trench with water.

³⁶ At the time of the evening offering, Elijah the prophet came near, and said, "Yahweh, the God of Abraham, of Isaac, and of Israel, let it be known today that you are God in Israel, and that I am your servant, and that I have done all these things at your word. ³⁷ Hear me, Yahweh, hear me, that this people may know that you, Yahweh, are God, and that you have turned their heart back again."

³⁸ Then Yahweh's fire fell, and consumed the burnt offering, the wood, the stones, and the dust, and licked up the water that was in the trench.

³⁹ When all the people saw it, they fell on their faces. They said, "Yahweh, he is God! Yahweh, he is God!"

⁴⁰ Elijah said to them, "Seize the prophets of Baal! Don't let one of them escape!" They seized them; and Elijah brought them down to the brook Kishon, and killed them there.

⁴¹ Elijah said to Ahab, "Get up, eat and drink; for there is the sound of abundance of rain."

⁴² So Ahab went up to eat and to drink. Elijah went up to the top of Carmel; and he bowed himself down on the earth, and put his face between his knees.

⁴³ He said to his servant, "Go up now, and look toward the sea." He went up, and looked, and said, "There is nothing." He said, "Go again" seven times.

⁴⁴ On the seventh time, he said, "Behold, a small cloud, like a man's hand, is rising out of the sea."

He said, "Go up, tell Ahab, 'Get ready and go down, so that the rain doesn't stop you.'" ⁴⁵ In a little while, the sky grew black with clouds and wind, and there was a great rain. Ahab rode, and went to Jezreel.

⁴⁶ Yahweh's hand was on Elijah; and he tucked his cloak into his belt and ran before Ahab to the entrance of Jezreel.

Saint Elijah, Church of Stella Maris,
Mt. Carmel, Haifa, Israel

December 16: Jonah and the Whale

Jonah was a prophet who became famous for being swallowed by a large fish or whale. God commanded Jonah to go to the city of Nineveh to tell the people that unless they repented God would destroy them for their sins. Jonah instead ran away and got on a boat going in the opposite direction. A big storm came up. The sailors knew it was not an ordinary storm and discovered that Jonah was to blame. Jonah admitted that it was his fault for disobeying God. They threw him overboard, and the storm calmed down. Jonah was saved by being swallowed by a great fish. Jonah prayed to God, and God commanded the fish to spit out Jonah. God again commanded Jonah to prophesy to Nineveh. This time he went and prophesied that in 40 days Nineveh would be overthrown. The people of Nineveh believed him, and the king and people fasted, prayed, and repented. God, who is very merciful, saw their repentant hearts and spared the people and the city.

"Jonah at the gates of Nineveh"
Hortus Deliciarum, c. 1180

Jonah 1:15-17. [15] So they took up Jonah, and threw him into the sea; and the sea ceased its raging. [16] Then the men feared Yahweh exceedingly; and they offered a sacrifice to Yahweh, and made vows. [17] Yahweh prepared a great fish to swallow up Jonah, and Jonah was in the belly of the fish three days and three nights.

Jonah 2:1-3. [1] Then Jonah prayed to Yahweh, his God, out of the fish's belly.
[2] He said, "I called because of my affliction to Yahweh. He answered me. Out of the belly of Sheol I cried. You heard my voice. [3] For you threw me into the depths, in the heart of the seas. The flood was all around me. All your waves and your billows passed over me.

Jonah 3:1-2. [1] Yahweh's word came to Jonah the second time, saying, [2] "Arise, go to Nineveh, that great city, and preach to it the message that I give you."

2:2 Sheol is the place of the dead.

December 17: Isaiah the Prophet

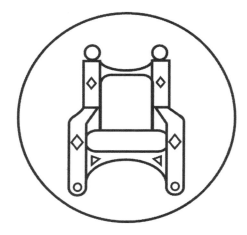

Isaiah was a prophet who had a vision of many things about God including the Lord sitting on high throne with angels around him. On having this vision he realized he was unclean and a sinner, but God forgave him and purified him from his sins. Then he heard God say, "Who shall we send?" And Isaiah said, "Here I am. Send me." Isaiah also foretold many things about the coming Messiah and what would happen in the future. He described the Messiah as a suffering servant as well as the nature, purpose, and details of his death long before Jesus was born. The book of Isaiah is quoted many times in the New Testament about how the Messiah would suffer, and that he would die to save many from their sins. He also foretold that the Messiah would be buried in a rich man's tomb and would be a light to the Gentiles.

"The Prophet Isaiah", Biblecard illustration, Providence Lithograph Company (c. 1904)

Isaiah 6:1-8. [1] In the year that King Uzziah died, I saw the Lord sitting on a throne, high and lifted up; and his train filled the temple. [2] Above him stood the seraphim. Each one had six wings. With two he covered his face. With two he covered his feet. With two he flew. [3] One called to another, and said, "Holy, holy, holy, is Yahweh of Armies! The whole earth is full of his glory!" [4] The foundations of the thresholds shook at the voice of him who called, and the house was filled with smoke. [5] Then I said, "Woe is me! For I am undone, because I am a man of unclean lips, and I dwell among a people of unclean lips: for my eyes have seen the King, Yahweh of Armies!"

[6] Then one of the seraphim flew to me, having a live coal in his hand, which he had taken with the tongs from off the altar. [7] He touched my mouth with it, and said, "Behold, this has touched your lips; and your iniquity is taken away, and your sin forgiven."

[8] I heard the Lord's voice, saying, "Whom shall I send, and who will go for us?" Then I said, "Here I am. Send me!"

Isaiah 49:6. "…I will also give you as a light to the nations, that you may be my salvation to the end of the earth."

Isaiah 53:3-5, 9. [3] He was despised, and rejected by men; a man of suffering, and acquainted with disease. He was despised as one from whom men hide their face; and we didn't respect him. [4] Surely he has borne our sickness, and carried our suffering; yet we considered him plagued, struck by God, and afflicted. [5] But he was pierced for our transgressions. He was crushed for our iniquities. The punishment that brought our peace was on him; and by his wounds we are healed…. [9] They made his grave with the wicked, and with a rich man in his death…

December 18: Daniel and the Lion

God allowed Jerusalem to be captured by the king of Babylon. Daniel and his three companions were taken to the palace for training. The king found them to be wise and kept them at his court. Later Daniel was elevated to a high office by King Darius, which made others jealous. Daniel's enemies tricked the king into ordering everyone not to worship any other god except for the king for 30 days, but Daniel did what was right and kept worshipping and praying to God instead. Due to the king's law, Daniel was thrown into a den of lions to be killed. But God protected Daniel from the lions, and he was not harmed.

"Daniel in the Lions' Den", Peter Paul Rubens, c. 1615

Daniel 6:7-23. [7] All the presidents of the kingdom, the deputies and the local governors, the counselors and the governors, have consulted together to establish a royal statute, and to make a strong decree, that whoever asks a petition of any god or man for thirty days, except of you, O king, he shall be cast into the den of lions. [8] Now, O king, establish the decree, and sign the writing, that it not be changed, according to the law of the Medes and Persians, which doesn't alter." [9] Therefore king Darius signed the writing and the decree.

[10] When Daniel knew that the writing was signed, he went into his house (now his windows were open in his room toward Jerusalem) and he kneeled on his knees three times a day, and prayed, and gave thanks before his God, as he did before. [11] Then these men assembled together, and found Daniel making petition and supplication before his God. [12] Then they came near, and spoke before the king concerning the king's decree: "Haven't you signed a decree that every man who makes a petition to any god or man within thirty days, except to you, O king, shall be cast into the den of lions?" The king answered, "This thing is true, according to the law of the Medes and Persians, which doesn't alter."

[13] Then they answered and said before the king, "That Daniel, who is of the children of the captivity of Judah, doesn't respect you, O king, nor the decree that you have signed, but makes his petition three times a day." [14] Then the king, when he heard these words, was very displeased, and set his heart on Daniel to deliver him; and he labored until the going down of the sun to rescue him. [15] Then these men assembled together to the king, and said to the king, "Know, O king, that it is a law of the Medes and Persians, that no decree nor statute which the king establishes may be changed."

[16] Then the king commanded, and they brought Daniel, and cast him into the den of lions. The king spoke and said to Daniel, "Your God whom you serve continually, he will deliver you."

[17] A stone was brought, and laid on the mouth of the den; and the king sealed it with his own signet, and with the signet of his lords; that nothing might be changed concerning Daniel. [18] Then the king went to his palace, and passed the night fasting. No musical instruments were brought before him; and his sleep fled from him. [19] Then the king arose very early in the morning, and went in haste to the den of lions. [20] When he came near to the den to Daniel, he cried with a troubled voice. The king spoke and said to Daniel, "Daniel, servant of the living God, is your God, whom you serve continually, able to deliver you from the lions?"

[21] Then Daniel said to the king, "O king, live forever! [22] My God has sent his angel, and has shut the lions' mouths, and they have not hurt me; because as before him innocence was found in me; and also before you, O king, I have done no harm." [23] Then the king was exceedingly glad, and commanded that they should take Daniel up out of the den. So Daniel was taken up out of the den, and no kind of harm was found on him, because he had trusted in his God.

December 19: Mary, Mother of Jesus

Mary is called the Blessed Mother because she is the mother of Jesus, and we call Mary *our mother too.* She is also known as the Blessed Virgin Mary. When she was a young teenager the Angel Gabriel appeared to her and told her she would be the mother of Jesus, the Messiah foretold by the prophets. Mary agreed and said, "Behold, the servant of the Lord; let it be done to me according to your word." Jesus is called the Messiah and our Savior because he is the only begotten son of God who became a man to save us from our sins and to reopen the gates of Heaven, which were closed by the first (original) sin of Adam and Eve. Mary is also called the New Eve and her son, Jesus, the New Adam. Whereas the first Adam and Eve lost Heaven for all of us, the New Adam who was born through the New Eve have brought salvation for all who are saved from their sins. Mary is considered to be the highest saint in Heaven and the Queen of Heaven. She was conceived without the stain of original sin on her soul by a special grace from God. Mary loves us as a mother and prays for us to God.

"The Annunciation"
Philippe de Champaigne, 1644

Luke 1:26-35, 38-60. ²⁶ Now in the sixth month, the angel Gabriel was sent from God to a city of Galilee, named Nazareth, ²⁷ to a virgin pledged to be married to a man whose name was Joseph, of David's house. The virgin's name was Mary.

²⁸ Having come in, the angel said to her, "Rejoice, you highly favored one! The Lord is with you. Blessed are you among women!"

²⁹ But when she saw him, she was greatly troubled at the saying, and considered what kind of salutation this might be.

³⁰ The angel said to her, "Don't be afraid, Mary, for you have found favor with God. ³¹ Behold, you will conceive in your womb, and give birth to a son, and will call his name 'Jesus.'

³² He will be great, and will be called the Son of the Most High. The Lord God will give him the throne of his father, David, ³³ and he will reign over the house of Jacob forever. There will be no end to his Kingdom."

³⁴ Mary said to the angel, "How can this be, seeing I am a virgin?"

³⁵ The angel answered her, "The Holy Spirit will come on you, and the power of the Most High will overshadow you. Therefore also the holy one who is born from you will be called the Son of God….

³⁸ Mary said, "Behold, the servant of the Lord; let it be done to me according to your word." The angel departed from her.

³⁹ Mary arose in those days and went into the hill country with haste, into a city of Judah, ⁴⁰ and entered into the house of Zacharias and greeted Elizabeth.

⁴¹ When Elizabeth heard Mary's greeting, the baby leaped in her womb, and Elizabeth was filled with the Holy Spirit.

⁴² She called out with a loud voice, and said, "Blessed are you among women, and blessed is the fruit of your womb!

⁴³ Why am I so favored, that the mother of my Lord should come to me? ⁴⁴ For behold, when the voice of your greeting came into my ears, the baby leaped in my womb for joy!

⁴⁵ Blessed is she who believed, for there will be a fulfillment of the things which have been spoken to her from the Lord!"

⁴⁶ Mary said, "My soul magnifies the Lord.

⁴⁷ My spirit has rejoiced in God my Savior, ⁴⁸ for he has looked at the humble state of his servant. For behold, from now on, all generations will call me blessed.

⁴⁹ For he who is mighty has done great things for me. Holy is his name.

⁵⁰ His mercy is for generations of generations on those who fear him.

⁵¹ He has shown strength with his arm. He has scattered the proud in the imagination of their hearts.

⁵² He has put down princes from their thrones. And has exalted the lowly.

⁵³ He has filled the hungry with good things. He has sent the rich away empty.

⁵⁴ He has given help to Israel, his servant, that he might remember mercy,

⁵⁵ As he spoke to our fathers, to Abraham and his offspring forever."

⁵⁶ Mary stayed with her about three months, and then returned to her house.

⁵⁷ Now the time that Elizabeth should give birth was fulfilled, and she gave birth to a son. ⁵⁸ Her neighbors and her relatives heard that the Lord had magnified his mercy towards her, and they rejoiced with her.

⁵⁹ On the eighth day, they came to circumcise the child; and they would have called him Zacharias, after the name of the father. ⁶⁰ His mother answered, "Not so; but he will be called John."

"The Visitation"
Domenico Ghirlandaio, 1491

87

December 20: Joseph, Stepfather of Jesus

Joseph was the stepfather of Jesus and the husband of Mary. He is a stepfather because Mary conceived Jesus by the Holy Spirit and not in the ordinary way. This took place while Mary was betrothed to Joseph but not yet married formally. At first when Joseph found out Mary was pregnant since he wasn't the father he was going to divorce her quietly. However, an angel told him through a dream that Mary's baby was conceived by the Holy Spirit and to take Mary as his wife. Joseph was a righteous man who obeyed God. He took care of his wife Mary and raised Jesus as a loving father. Joseph made a living as a carpenter who worked with wood and other materials. He also taught Jesus how to be a carpenter.

"Saint Joseph with Child Jesus"
Caspar Jele, 1848, Germany

Matthew 1:18-24. [18] Now the birth of Jesus Christ was like this: After his mother, Mary, was engaged to Joseph, before they came together, she was found pregnant by the Holy Spirit. [19] Joseph, her husband, being a righteous man, and not willing to make her a public example, intended to put her away secretly. [20] But when he thought about these things, behold, an angel of the Lord appeared to him in a dream, saying, "Joseph, son of David, don't be afraid to take to yourself Mary, your wife, for that which is conceived in her is of the Holy Spirit. [21] She shall give birth to a son. You shall call his name Jesus, for it is he who shall save his people from their sins."

[22] Now all this has happened, that it might be fulfilled which was spoken by the Lord through the prophet, saying, [23] "Behold, the virgin shall be with child, and shall give birth to a son. They shall call his name Immanuel;" which is, being interpreted, "God with us."

[24] Joseph arose from his sleep, and did as the angel of the Lord commanded him, and took his wife to himself...

December 21: John the Baptist

The priest Zacharias and his wife Elizabeth, who was a relative of Jesus, were upright people but unable to have a child. Then one day the Angel Gabriel appeared to Zacharias. He said that God had heard their prayers and they would have a son and were to name him John. Their child would be filled with the Holy Spirit and would have the power of the prophet Elijah to prepare the way for the Messiah. Mary went and stayed with Elizabeth and when John was born there was great rejoicing. When John grew up he became strong with the spirit and he preached Baptism for the remission of sins. He also baptized Jesus, though Jesus was without sin, in the River Jordan.

"St. John the Baptist in the Wilderness"
Jusepe de Ribera, c. 1635, Italy

Luke 1:5-23. ⁵ There was in the days of Herod, the king of Judea, a certain priest named Zacharias, of the priestly division of Abijah. He had a wife of the daughters of Aaron, and her name was Elizabeth. ⁶ They were both righteous before God, walking blamelessly in all the commandments and ordinances of the Lord. ⁷ But they had no child, … and they both were well advanced in years. ⁸ Now while he executed the priest's office before God in the order of his division, ⁹ according to the custom of the priest's office, his lot was to enter into the temple of the Lord and burn incense. ¹⁰ The whole multitude of the people were praying outside at the hour of incense.

¹¹ An angel of the Lord appeared to him, standing on the right side of the altar of incense. ¹² Zacharias was troubled when he saw him, and fear fell upon him. ¹³ But the angel said to him, "Don't be afraid, Zacharias, because your request has been heard, and your wife, Elizabeth, will bear you a son, and you shall call his name John. ¹⁴ You will have joy and gladness; and many will rejoice at his birth. ¹⁵ For he will be great in the sight of the Lord, and he will drink no wine nor strong drink. He will be filled with the Holy Spirit, even from his mother's womb. ¹⁶ He will turn many of the children of Israel to the Lord, their God. ¹⁷ He will go before him in the spirit and power of Elijah, 'to turn the hearts of the fathers to the children,' and the disobedient to the wisdom of the just; to prepare a people prepared for the Lord."

¹⁸ Zacharias said to the angel, "How can I be sure of this? For I am an old man, and my wife is well advanced in years." ¹⁹ The angel answered him, "I am Gabriel, who stands in the presence of God. I was sent to speak to you, and to bring you this good news. ²⁰ Behold, you will be silent and not able to speak, until the day that these things will happen, because you didn't believe my words, which will be fulfilled in their proper time." ²¹ The people were waiting for Zacharias, and they marveled that he delayed in the temple. ²² When he came out, he could not speak to them, and they perceived that he had seen a vision in the temple. He continued making signs to them, and remained mute. ²³ When the days of his service were fulfilled, he departed to his house.

Luke 1: 36-37. ³⁶ Behold, Elizabeth, your relative, also has conceived a son in her old age; and this is the sixth month with her who was called barren. ³⁷ For nothing spoken by God is impossible.

Luke 3:3. He came into all the region around the Jordan, preaching the baptism of repentance for remission of sins.

Matthew 3:13. Then Jesus came from Galilee to the Jordan to John, to be baptized by him.

December 22: Bethlehem, the birthplace of Jesus

The Bible tells us that Jesus Christ was born in the town of Bethlehem. A long time before Jesus was born the prophets had foretold that the Messiah would be born there. At that time Caesar Augustus, the Roman ruler in those days, wanted everyone to report for a census in their own city. Joseph in obedience to the law took Mary to Bethlehem, which was the City of David where their ancestors were from. It is while they were there that Jesus was born. There was also a special star in the sky over Bethlehem. Wise men from the east saw this star and travelled from a far away country in hopes of seeing the newborn King.

View of Bethlehem, 1898, (with star added)

Luke 2:1-5. [1] Now in those days, a decree went out from Caesar Augustus that all the world should be enrolled. [2] This was the first enrollment made when Quirinius was governor of Syria. [3] All went to enroll themselves, everyone to his own city. [4] Joseph also went up from Galilee, out of the city of Nazareth, into Judea, to David's city, which is called Bethlehem, because he was of the house and family of David; [5] to enroll himself with Mary, who was pledged to be married to him as wife, being pregnant.

Matthew 2:1-6, 11. [1] Now when Jesus was born in Bethlehem of Judea in the days of King Herod, behold, wise men from the east came to Jerusalem, saying, [2] "Where is he who is born King of the Jews? For we saw his star in the east, and have come to worship him."

[3] When King Herod heard it, he was troubled, and all Jerusalem with him. [4] Gathering together all the chief priests and scribes of the people, he asked them where the Christ would be born.

[5] They said to him, "In Bethlehem of Judea, for this is written through the prophet, [6] 'You Bethlehem, land of Judah, are in no way least among the princes of Judah: for out of you shall come a governor, who shall shepherd my people, Israel.'" ...

[11] They came into the house and saw the young child with Mary, his mother, and they fell down and worshiped him. Opening their treasures, they offered to him gifts: gold, frankincense, and myrrh.

December 23: Angels Proclaim the Birth of Jesus

Angels are spiritual beings. When God created the angels, he gave them free will just like he does with people. He let them choose if they wanted to love and obey God, and live with God in Heaven or not. The good angels chose to love God and obey him. The bad angels disobeyed God and are now called devils. The good angels are happy and serve God and his people. Some of them are our guardian angels. Sometimes angels bring messages from God. On the night that Jesus was born there were shepherds in the fields watching their sheep. An angel appeared to them telling them not to be afraid as he brought "good news of great joy". He said that today in the City of David, a Savior had been born who is Christ the Lord. Then many angels appeared praising God and singing, "Glory to God in the highest and on earth peace to men of good will."

"The Angel's Song, illustration from
The Boyhood of Jesus, by Anonymous, 1905

Luke 2:8-14. [8] There were shepherds in the same country staying in the field, and keeping watch by night over their flock. [9] Behold, an angel of the Lord stood by them, and the glory of the Lord shone around them, and they were terrified.

[10] The angel said to them, "Don't be afraid, for behold, I bring you good news of great joy which will be to all the people. [11] For there is born to you today, in David's city, a Savior, who is Christ the Lord. [12] This is the sign to you: you will find a baby wrapped in strips of cloth, lying in a feeding trough."

[13] Suddenly, there was with the angel a multitude of the heavenly army praising God, and saying, [14] "Glory to God in the highest, on earth peace, good will toward men."

"Sistine Madonna" (detail of angels), Rafael, 1513-14

91

December 24: The Birth of Christ on Christmas Day

Jesus Christ was born on the first Christmas day. He is the Messiah or Savior foretold by the prophets. Jesus was born in a cave where animals lived because when Joseph and Mary arrived in Bethlehem for a census there was no room for them to stay at the inn. Mary wrapped Jesus in swaddling clothes and laid him in a manger. After the angels appeared to the shepherds tending their flocks, the shepherds came to see Jesus. They praised and glorified God and told many people the Messiah had been born. Also the wise men from the east, who had followed the special star, were so happy to find Jesus with his mother Mary that "they fell down and worshipped him". Then they gave Jesus treasures of gold, frankincense, and myrrh. Mary kept all these things in her heart and pondered all that had happened.

"Adoration of the Shepherds"
Gerard von Honthorst, 1622

Luke 2:6-7, 13-20. [6] While they were there, the day had come for her to give birth. [7] She gave birth to her firstborn son. She wrapped him in bands of cloth, and laid him in a feeding trough, because there was no room for them in the inn….

[13] Suddenly, there was with the angel a multitude of the heavenly army praising God, and saying, [14] "Glory to God in the highest, on earth peace, good will toward men." [15] When the angels went away from them into the sky, the shepherds said to one another, "Let's go to Bethlehem, now, and see this thing that has happened, which the Lord has made known to us."

[16] They came with haste, and found both Mary and Joseph, and the baby was lying in the feeding trough. [17] When they saw it, they publicized widely the saying which was spoken to them about this child. [18] All who heard it wondered at the things which were spoken to them by the shepherds. [19] But Mary kept all these sayings, pondering them in her heart. [20] The shepherds returned, glorifying and praising God for all the things that they had heard and seen, just as it was told them.

Matthew 2:7-12. [7] Then Herod secretly called the wise men… [8] He sent them to Bethlehem… [9] They, having heard the king, went their way; and behold, the star, which they saw in the east, went before them, until it came and stood over where the young child was. [10] When they saw the star, they rejoiced with exceedingly great joy. [11] They came into the house and saw the young child with Mary, his mother, and they fell down and worshiped him. Opening their treasures, they offered to him gifts: gold, frankincense, and myrrh. [12] Being warned in a dream that they shouldn't return to Herod, they went back to their own country another way.

Blank Ornaments:

These ornaments and those on the next pages may be used if you would like to draw some of your own.

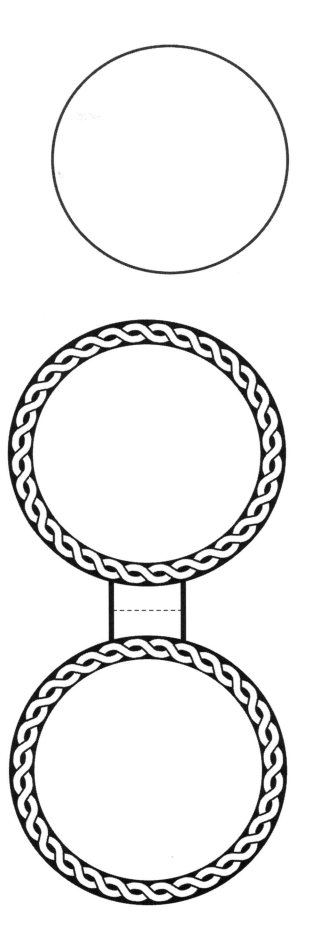

Blank Ornaments:

These ornaments may be used if you
would like to draw some of your own.

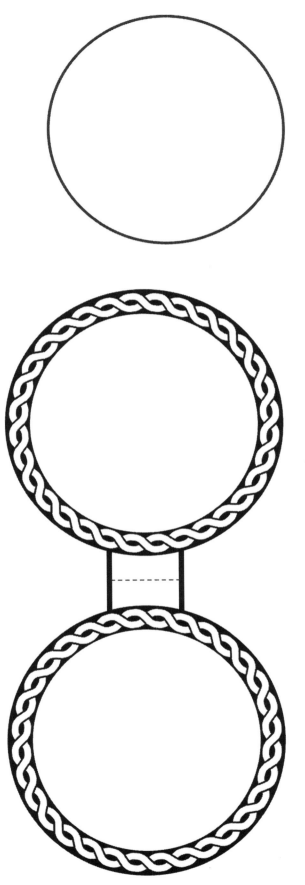

95

Blank Ornaments:

These ornaments may be used if you would like to draw some of your own.

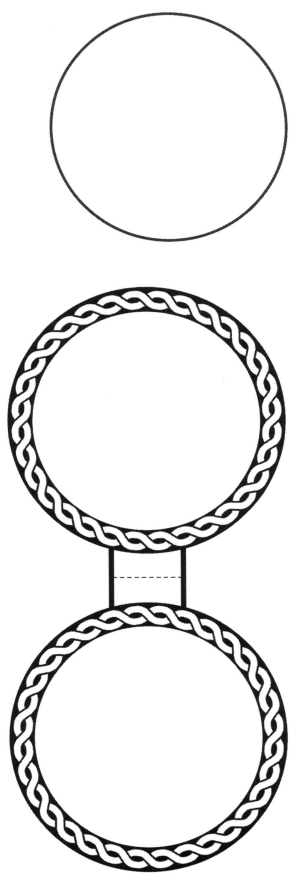

Blank Ornaments:

These ornaments may be used if you would like to draw some of your own.

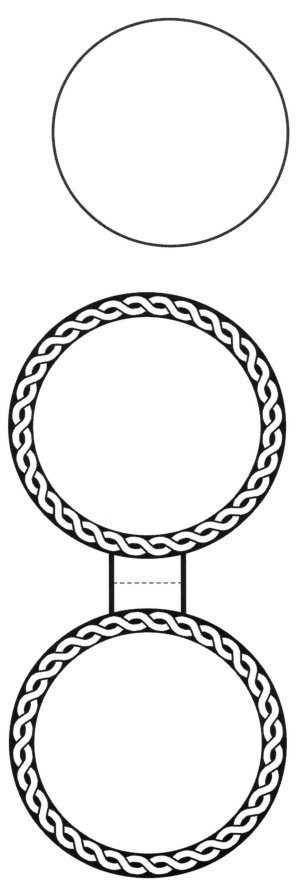

47520577R00062

Made in the USA
Middletown, DE
27 August 2017